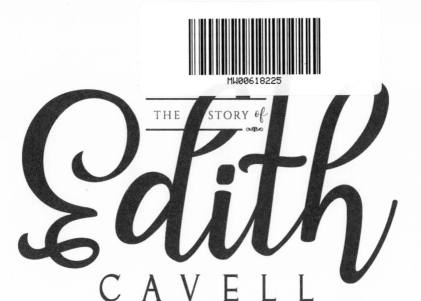

THE STORY of
Edith
CAVELL

By Iris Vinton

Illustrated by Gerald McCann

In friendship and gratitude, the author makes acknowledgement to:

Charlotte Seymour Day, Librarian, English Speaking Union, and Secretary, Books Across the Sea Committee, for locating biographical material in the United States and in England;

Miriam Y. Holden, whose private library on Woman's Role in Civilization was a valuable source of information on women and the times, and on the nursing profession in the different countries involved;

Ruth Isaacs, Librarian, British Information Services, who made various books and pamphlets available;

Edward J. and Charles A. O'Malley, of O'Malley's Book Store, who made a special search for certain rare books and materials on the subject.

Edith's brother Jack and sister Lilian appeared

CONTENTS

CHAPTER I

Edith

EDITH finished dusting the books that lined one wall of the study. She stepped back to see if they were straight on the shelves. One book stuck out from the others.

"You are spoiling your row," she scolded it kindly. And she gave it a gentle push into place.

Nothing annoyed her father, the Reverend Frederick Cavell, Vicar of Swardeston, so much as dust or any kind of disorder. He particularly disliked to have Ellen, who came each day to help Mrs. Cavell with the housework, tidy his study.

"She never puts things back in their proper places," he grumbled. "And she moves things on my desk. Now, Edith puts everything back exactly the way she finds it."

The vicar's likes and dislikes were very important

to his family. Since she was ten years old, Edith had been cleaning her father's study. She was eleven going on twelve now. And it was still her daily chore while Papa took his early morning walk. It was during his morning exercise that he thought out problems.

To sweep and dust did not take Edith long. But today, it seemed to take twice as long as usual. It was always that way when she was in a hurry. Florence, her older sister, would have helped. But she was busy in the kitchen, helping their mother make strawberry jam.

Edith scowled at the bowl of roses on the reading table. The lamp almost hid them from anyone sitting at the desk. Her father loved flowers as he loved music, poetry, painting, and the old church among the trees where he preached. She moved the roses away from the lamp so that he could see them when he worked at his desk.

There was a polite knock, and the study door opened. Her brother Jack and sister Lilian appeared. Their round faces looked cross, and they were in a bad temper.

"We have been waiting and waiting and *waiting*," complained her brother.

"You aren't even ready to go *yet*," accused her sister, who was usually good natured.

Edith smiled at them cheerfully. "I'll be ready in three minutes," she promised. She untied her apron. At the same time, she gave a final glance round the room.

The breeze from the open window had scattered papers on the desk. She ran over, put them in a neat pile, and set a paperweight on top. Glancing down, she saw they were notes her father had made for his sermon on Sunday. The first note caught her eye, and, without thinking, she read it aloud.

"Sermon for next Sunday," she read. "Psalms 119, Verse 163: I hate and abhor lying."

"Oh, gloom, gloom, gloom!" exclaimed Lilian. "I wish Papa wouldn't preach on gloomy things all the time. I like to hear about cheerful subjects."

"Papa doesn't want to be gloomy," Edith said, "but some people lie and cheat and steal. And they are mean and cruel to one another. So Papa has to speak out against all this wrongdoing. Don't you understand?"

"I suppose," sighed Lilian.

"When are we going, Edith?" Jack asked irritably. "I want to go now."

"Go sit on the front step, and I'll be there in no time," Edith said. "While you wait, you can watch the people going by on their way to Norwich. It's always amusing to see people going to market."

She shooed them out the study door and down the hall. As she ran upstairs to her room, she could hear them grumbling to each other. They threatened to go off without her if she did not hurry.

In her room, Edith hung up her apron and got out her big straw hat. The August sun was very hot. She washed her face and brushed her shining light brown hair. Standing in front of the mirror, she put on her hat. Her blue eyes examined her reflection: cotton dress, spotless; stockings, unwrinkled; shoes, shined. Everything was neat and trim as always.

Today, she and the children, Lilian and Jack, were going blackberrying with some friends. For such a jaunt, many girls might wear a soiled dress or unpolished shoes—but not Edith. Her clothes might be mended and patched, but they were always as clean and fresh as if she were going to a party.

Of course, blackberrying was as much fun as a party. The work of picking berries was play when friends did it together. And she and Lilian and Jack would bring home lots of sweet, wild blackberries to be made into jam for the winter. The Cavells used a great deal of jam, and it was needed also to fill jars for the many baskets that the vicarage sent to poor people at Christmas.

Edith hurried downstairs and into the kitchen. Her mother and Florence were stirring big kettles of bubbling strawberries. At Edith's entrance, they turned around.

"Are you and the children ready?" asked her mother.

"Yes, Mama, we're going now," Edith answered. She sniffed the spicy air. "Umm, smells good."

"That's your lunch basket on the table," Florence said. She brushed a strand of brown hair back from her forehead. "Oh, this heat does make me feel grubby! I put in an extra piece of saffron cake for each of you."

"You are a dear!" Edith cried. "I do love saffron cake." She hung the lunch basket on one arm. Then she took the three tin pails for berries from the sideboard and hung them over the other arm.

Mrs. Cavell watched her pretty, graceful daughter with a fond smile. Her eyes sparkled with amusement as Edith added to her load.

"Do you think you will need three pails?" Mrs. Cavell asked. "You know, Jack will probably eat all the berries he picks."

"Oh, it makes him feel grown up to have a pail," Edith told her with a grin. "Well, I'm off," she added. She started toward the door, with a clink and clatter.

"Be careful," Mrs. Cavell warned. "I'm sure that Miss Bab is a responsible young lady and will look after you girls and boys, but I depend on you to take care of your little brother and sister."

"Yes, Mama, I will," Edith promised.

"And don't be late for tea," Florence called after her. "You know it makes Papa cross for anyone to be late for tea."

"We'll start back in plenty of time," Edith answered.

She found Jack and Lilian still waiting on the front step and gave each one a pail. Then all three set out from the vicarage for the old Gowthorpe Manor near the village green, where they were to meet the other berry pickers.

CHAPTER II

The Blackberry Picking

BECAUSE today was market day in Norwich, four miles away, there was much noise and confusion in Swardeston. The little village lay beside the highway, and farmers on their way to Norwich went rattling through Swardeston in carts and wagons filled with flowers, fruits, and vegetables to sell in the big marketplace. Sheep and cattle were driven past the village green, with their bells playing jangled music to a chorus of *baas* and *moos*.

Edith, Lilian, and Jack stood at the edge of the green to wait for a flock to pass.

A sheepdog barked sharply. Half a dozen sheep had broken away from the flock in the road and were trotting across the green. The dog was after them, nipping at their heels to keep them together.

"Bring them back, boy! Bring them back!" shouted

the farmer. He gave a peculiar whistle. The dog circled the stray sheep and turned them back toward the road.

Edith watched, fascinated as always by a sheepdog at work. It was amazing how he could straighten out confused and bewildered sheep and head them in the right direction.

"Oh, I wish I had a dog like that!" she cried. "Oh, how I'd love to have a dog!"

"A dog would be nice," agreed Lilian. But she was not, at the moment, interested in dogs. She wanted to pick blackberries. "We had better hurry," she warned. "The others will leave us behind."

"Yes, we had better hurry," echoed Jack.

They crossed the highway and turned down a little side street that led to Gowthorpe Manor. The manor was an ancient house with a moat or ditch around it. The moat had long since gone dry, and its sides had fallen in.

When Edith, Lilian, and Jack came up the walk, they saw a group of boys rushing across the ditch.

"Charge the castle!" the boys shouted. "To the walls, men!" They rushed for the garden wall of the manor and scaled to the top by climbing on one another's shoulders.

Several girls stood watching them in envy. If it were not thought unladylike, they would have been scaling the walls themselves.

Miss Bab, the young lady in charge of the blackberry pickers, smacked her hands together sharply. "Now, boys! Boys, come! No more of that!" she commanded.

Just then the group caught sight of Edith and Lilian and Jack. They shouted, "Hello! Hello there!"

The three waved their pails gaily in answer. Then, quickly breaking away from Edith, Jack ran toward the boys.

Edith called, "Come back! Jack, you mustn't climb on the wall!"

But he was too excited to listen. On he went, across the little hollow where the old moat had been. Suddenly, he stumbled and fell. He gave a shriek that made Edith drop her basket and pail and run down to him.

The boys dropped down off the wall like so many falling apples. Miss Bab and the girls rushed down in a flutter of skirts. They all crowded around.

Jack lay on his stomach, howling. Edith knelt down and felt him all over. She could find no broken bones. He surely could not have hurt himself very much by a tumble in the soft grass.

"What happened, Jack? Did something frighten you? Tell sister," Edith pleaded.

"I—I stepped on a tremendous snake!" Jack burst out.

"Oh, I don't think it could have been a very big snake," Edith said. "We have nice little green garden snakes in Swardeston."

"Dear me," said Miss Bab. "He might have been bitten."

"I don't think so, Miss Bab," Edith assured her in a grown-up voice. "There isn't any swelling anywhere. Besides, my father says there are almost no poisonous snakes in England."

"He didn't bite me," Jack declared, sitting up suddenly. "When I stepped on him, he hissed at me and ran away."

"Then everything is quite all right," said Miss Bab. "Come along, everybody."

Edith handed Jack a handkerchief. He wiped the dirt and tears from his face and stood up. Soon, swinging lunch baskets and tin pails, they all set out for a wooded lane near the manor. When they reached the first berry patch, they fell to picking the fruit with gleeful cries. At first they ate all they picked. Then slowly the pails began to fill up.

For lunch, Miss Bab led the children to a cool spot beneath some trees. They spread out the contents of their baskets on the grass.

Bread, cheese, boiled eggs, sausages, jelly tarts, and cakes disappeared in no time. Several boys declared themselves still famished. So Edith, Lilian, and Jack parted with their second pieces of saffron cake. As the vicar's children, they were expected to set a good example of sharing with others. They always did, although at times not as cheerfully as their father might have wished.

After lunch, a hunt for more well-filled bushes led them to a rich patch near a brook. The branches dropped to the ground with black, ripe berries. Whooping, the boys and girls started to pick.

"Well, I must say," declared Miss Bab, "at this rate, we shall fill our pails and our baskets, too. There will be berries and jam enough for all the people of Swardeston—all three hundred of them!"

Edith wandered beside the brook, looking for still more bushes. She had gone a good way without finding any, when she came to a patch along a stone fence. She could hear a soft tinkle of bells. There must be a flock of sheep in the pasture.

As she started to pick berries, she heard two men working and talking on the other side of the fence. The brook which ran through the pasture was clogged with twigs and leaves. The men were busy clearing it.

All of a sudden one man exclaimed, "Well, look who's here! And she has brought her puppies, too! Good dog, Mab!"

"She had to carry one of them," said the other man.

"Yes, the poor, weak thing!" cried the first man. "It's a great pity, but we will have to do away with that puppy. There's something terribly wrong with it."

"Ay, a sickness in its chest," the second man said with a sigh. "I think I'd better drown it in the morning."

Edith felt her head swim. They were going to drown a puppy! In her imagination, she could see them putting it in a dark sack filled with stones. It would sink to the bottom of the brook that ran at her feet.

"No! No!" she cried. "You mustn't!"

But the men did not hear her. At that moment, there was a great jangling of sheep bells, and the dog started barking.

"It's that goat!" declared one of the men. "He's got the gate open again. There go the sheep after him. Go! Get 'em, Mab! Fetch them back, Mab!"

There came the sounds of men running and the dog, Mab, barking furiously.

Edith was over the fence, quick as a squirrel. Men and dog were halfway to the other end of the pasture. Three puppies were hurrying on unsteady legs after them. A fourth puppy lay whimpering on the grass.

Edith crouched down and let the puppy sniff her fingers. It stopped whimpering and looked up at her. She petted it gently. With great effort, it struggled to its feet.

"Poor, sick baby," Edith said. Then, getting up, she began to back away. It followed her, dragging its weak legs. She backed farther and farther away. It still followed. She stepped back, back, toward the fence. At the fence she stopped, and it came tumbling onto her feet.

It had followed her. Edith's heart jumped with excitement. The puppy had come to her. She must save it. She scooped it up.

The next moment she was over the fence and flying back along the brook, the puppy held close to her, and her berry pail thumping against her side.

When she could run no longer, she sat down by the side of the brook. Holding the puppy in her lap, she stroked its scrawny little body.

"You are safe now," she crooned under her breath. "They'll never find you. There, they can't harm you now."

It closed its eyes peacefully.

Edith was so intent on comforting the puppy that she scarcely noticed the berry pickers. It was only when she heard a boy cry, "Oh, look what Edith's found!" that she realized the children were surrounding her.

"Why, it's a puppy!" exclaimed Miss Bab. "Now, I wonder where it could have come from."

"Some farmers probably wanted to get rid of it," one of the children said, "so he left it by the road on his way to Norwich."

"More likely some cruel and thoughtless tramp or peddler," said Miss Bab angrily. "It is dreadful to think of the many kittens and puppies people have left by the wayside to starve."

"Oh, Edith!" Lilian cried. "You wanted a puppy, and now you've found one."

She and Jack dropped to their knees in front of Edith. They touched the puppy shyly with a finger. The others stood around admiring it.

"Are you going to keep it, Edith?" a boy asked.

"Of course I am," she declared.

Miss Bab glanced at the sun halfway down the western sky. "We must get started back, children," she said. "I promised to have you all home by teatime. Gather up your things."

They were soon ready. And laden with pails and

baskets of blackberries, the flock of children started up the lane for home. They trudged along silently, tired and happy.

Edith walked in their midst as though she were in a dream. She scarcely felt the weight of two pails of berries, which she had hung with a cord over her shoulder. And the puppy in her arms might have been a feather, he seemed so light.

At the village green, the children parted and went their different ways. When Edith, Lilian, and Jack came through the gate at the back of the vicarage, they found their father and mother sitting on a bench under the trees.

"Ah, there you are!" exclaimed Mrs. Cavell. "And look at all the berries you've picked!"

"Look, Mama! Look, Papa!" Jack cried. "See what Edith has!"

Mr. Cavell's stern face turned to Edith. "I declare, if it isn't a puppy! And where did you get that?"

Edith's tongue felt glued to the roof of her mouth. She dared not tell her father how she had got it. He would call it stealing. And his anger would be terrible. He would make her take the puppy back. Take it back to be drowned? Oh, no!

"I found it near the lane, Papa," she said quickly.

There, it was out. She had told a lie. She expected the ground to crumble beneath her feet.

Then, as if from a great distance, she heard Jack pipe up, "We think someone left it by the road. And Edith found it and brought it home."

"Ah, poor thing. Well, it will find a warm welcome here," said Mr. Cavell.

CHAPTER III

Sunday and Tears

THE next morning was Sunday. Edith was woken up at six o'clock by the puppy's whimpering. The night before she had lined up a box with soft rags and placed it on the floor beside her. Resting her cheek on the edge of the bed, she peered down at the little thing, nibbling at the rags. She reached out one hand and stroked the puppy as though it were made of glass and might break at a touch. It cried piteously.

"Of course, you are hungry," she soothed him.

She got up, washed, and dressed quietly. Picking the puppy up, box and all, she tiptoed downstairs to the kitchen. She started a fire in the stove and put some milk on to warm.

While she waited, she sat on the floor and gazed at him. "You are too little to be cuddled, Papa says," she told him.

She petted his ear with a finger. He was a weak, scrawny creature. But these failings only endeared him to Edith, who longed to make him strong and well.

The milk was warm. Twisting a bit of cloth into a nipple, Edith dipped it into the milk. With the puppy cupped in her arm, she gave the cloth to him to suck. He closed his eyes and sucked, not greedily as most healthy puppies do, but listlessly. She kept dipping the cloth into the milk, and soon he had had enough. Yet his tiny paunch was not round with milk as most puppies' bellies are when they have had their fill.

When he refused to take any more milk, Edith put the puppy in his box and carried it out in the back of the house to her favorite place beneath the apple tree.

Returning to the house, she set the table for breakfast. She moved in a sort of daze, her mind busy trying to find a name for the puppy. After a while, she heard her mother and father, Florence, Lilian, and Jack come downstairs. Her father called, "Edith!"

She hurried to the hallway and knelt down with the family for morning prayers. Her father prayed longer on Sunday than on any other day. But the hard oak boards might have been cushions beneath her knees for all she felt them today.

After breakfast, the vicar went for his walk. As usual, he took the path that led from the vicarage garden through the ancient cemetery and up to the church. Back and forth he walked, thinking and praying. His mind burned with the fiery words he would use in his sermon against the evil things in the world.

While her father went over his sermon as he paced up and down, Edith helped her mother and sisters put the house in order. She did her chores as quickly as she could without slighting them. Then she took a little warm milk in a cup to the puppy.

"Sleep now until I get back," she told him.

The bells rang for morning service. Edith, in front

with Jack, and her mother and sisters behind her, started up the path to church.

It was almost half past ten. Groups of neighbors and farmers' families were crossing the green. At the door of the church, they stopped to exchange greetings with the vicar's wife. Mrs. Cavell, warmhearted and cheerful, was a great favorite with everyone in Swardeston.

Seated with her mother, sisters, and brother in their pew near the front of the church, Edith listened to the organist playing softly. It made her feel quiet and peaceful inside. The music grew louder. Then gradually it faded away.

Edith saw her father take his place before the congregation. For a moment he stood silent, his head up. Then his deep voice rose in prayer.

The familiar sound of her father's voice sent Edith's thoughts flying back to yesterday. Across her memory flashed a picture of herself, holding her hand out to the puppy. She was stepping slowly backward, luring it on. And now she was running away with it.

Her thoughts leaped. She saw herself as though she were in the body of some strange girl. And the girl was holding up a puppy and saying, "I found it, Papa."

That strange girl was herself, Edith Cavell. The lie stuck in her throat and choked her. The people were singing a hymn. But no sounds came when she tried to sing. The voices swelled into a loud "Amen." The Vicar mounted the pulpit.

"The text for my sermon today is from Psalms," he announced. "My text is five words from the Bible: 'I hate and abhor lying.'" He paused. Then, in ringing tones, he began, "He who tells a lie once finds it easier to lie a second time, and a third time, and a fourth. Then it becomes a habit. He tells a lie without thinking. Even when he tells the truth, he is no longer believed. Lies of the tongue lead to lies in heart and thoughts. It is the coward who lies. He fears the truth. The brave do not lie. Truth being truth, they tell it, 'though they die for it!'"

Edith felt herself trembling. She was horrified at the thought of how she had deceived her friends, her brother and sisters, and her mother and father about the puppy. And it seemed to her that from the pulpit, her father was accusing her of lying. Accusing her only!

His voice roared as an angry river in her ears.

At last the sermon was over. People were getting up, leaving the church. Like a puppet made of wood, Edith walked with the people down the aisle and out the door. She fled down the path toward home as though something pursued her. Reaching the apple tree in the yard, she flung herself down beside the

puppy's box. Her heart turned to wax inside of her
at the sight of him curled up asleep. She sat rocking
back and forth, crooning softly to him.

Voices close by brought Edith back to herself. She
heard her father say, "You would know the puppy, of
course."

"I could not mistake it," answered a man's voice she
had heard yesterday in the pasture. "There are none
as has sheepdogs like mine in these parts."

In panic, Edith grabbed up the puppy. With it
clutched against her, she stood facing her father.
With him were Mr. Peters and his son, Hal, a boy of
fifteen. They came to church in Swardeston several
times a year, although they regularly
went to Norwich Cathedral.

Mr. Peters eyed the dog. "Ay, that's
him all right," he declared. "Hal heard
some boys talking earlier this morning in the churchyard
about picking black-
berries yesterday

near the sheep pasture. Edith, the vicar's girl, had
found a puppy, they said. Struck me, it might be the
one missing from Mab's litter. And so it is."

"It's too bad, dear," said Mr. Cavell. "But you must
give it back to Mr. Peters."

"But he's going to drown it. I heard him say so!"
she cried. "I can't let him, Papa!"

She saw her father's face become stony as he
realized she had lied to him about finding the puppy.
His own daughter!

"Give it to Mr. Peters, Edith," he told her coldly.

She handed it to the farmer. She could feel the
tears sliding down her cheeks. "Oh, I love it so!" she
burst out.

"Why, the poor thing will be better off dead," Mr.
Peters consoled her. "It has a bad sickness. See, it can
hardly breathe. All the care in the world can't save it."

"We can't let you keep it," Hal explained kindly.
"The disease might be catching."

Mr. Peters cleared his throat. "Well, we'll be
getting along, Vicar," he said. "Good day to you both."

"Good day, Mr. Peters. Goodbye, Hal," replied Mr.
Cavell. When they were gone, he spoke to Edith. He
appeared calm, but she could tell he was shocked and
angry.

"I am not going to punish you," he said quietly.
"After what has happened, I doubt that you'll be

tempted to tell a lie again soon." He walked away from her.

Sobbing, Edith ran to the house and up to her room. She threw herself across the bed. Her head was spinning, and she thought she was going to be sick. After a while the feeling passed.

She heard the family moving about, but no one came near her. She had never felt so lonely and miserable in her life. She tried reading from her Prayer Book, but her thoughts were too confused to follow the words.

She got out her drawing pad and pencil finally. Settling the pad on her lap, she began to sketch. She drew dogs and sheep, puppies and lambs. She filled page after page until she was exhausted. Then, with a little sigh, she fell asleep.

CHAPTER IV

Wednesday and the Peterses

For several days, Edith was very unhappy.
She and her father had hurt each other very
much. Now, for fear of being hurt again, they
avoided each other as much as possible. And it
seemed neither one of them could find the words
which would break the spell.

Wednesday morning came. As usual, at a quarter
past eight, Edith went with her books to the study
for lessons with her brother and sisters.

The vicar taught his own and some of the children
of his parish. But it was summertime. And, except
for the Cavells, boys and girls in Swardeston were
done with lessons.

Florence, Lilian, and Jack were outside in the yard.
Their voices came through the open windows as they
hunted for beetles for Jack's collection.

The Vicar sat at his desk, busy with ruler, pencil, and a piece of paper. He frowned and made little sounds of impatience as he worked. When Edith entered, the frown quickly vanished.

"Come here, my dear," he said. "I need your help. The guild is holding a flower show, and the ladies asked me if I would make an announcement to place

in the vestibule of the church. I'm afraid I'm making a mess of it." He shook his head sadly.

The sun was bright again for Edith. Her heart felt light for the first time in days. "Of course, I'll help you, Papa."

The spell was broken at last. Both of them were cheerful and lively as they worked. Edith printed the letters carefully. Then she drew a border of flowers with bees and butterflies hovering about.

"Now, that is quite pretty indeed," her father praised her. "I think it is almost good enough to show your art teacher."

Once a week a young artist came from Norwich to give lessons in drawing and painting to a few of the young ladies in the village. Edith had very early shown a talent for drawing, and her father had sent her to the weekly class. Mr. Cavell was proud of his daughter's work.

"I'll get my paints," she said, "and color the flowers."

"Later," said Mr. Cavell. "It's past time for lessons. We had better get on with them."

Edith started to call the others, but Florence appeared, herding the two younger ones before her. They took their places on the low stools in front of their father's desk. They put their books on the floor beside them and placed their writing boards on their laps. And lessons began.

While Jack read aloud a story about King Arthur, Florence, Edith, and Lilian did their exercises in English grammar. Their father kept four lessons going at the same time.

When he left off with Jack in addition and subtraction, he took up with Lilian doing multiplication. Then on he went to Edith with weights and measures, and finally to Florence with problems about papering rooms and carpeting floors.

Round and round they went, each reciting in turn. Shortly before lunchtime, they heard a horse and cart enter the drive and go around to the back of the house.

"I wonder who that is," Jack said. "Shall I go see who it is, Papa?"

"Your mother is in the kitchen. She will take care of everything," answered his father. "Don't be impatient. You have only a few more lines to do in your copybook."

Jack sighed loudly.

Out of the corner of her eye, Edith read the time. It lacked three minutes of being half past eleven and the end of school for the day. She bent her head again to her history book.

The clock's works began to grind and whirr in readiness to strike the half hour. Then exactly on the solemn bong, as if on cue in a play, there was a clamor in the hall and the study door flew open.

An overgrown shepherd puppy bounded into the study. He stood stock still at the sight of the five. One ear went up and the other down while he stared at them, his tongue lolling out the side of his mouth.

Behind him were Mr. Peters and his son, Hal, grinning sheepishly. And back of them was Mrs. Cavell, looking dismayed and amused by turns.

"Sorry, Vicar," apologized Mr. Peters, "to burst in on you like this. But Don, here, can't stand closed doors. Has to see what's on the other side."

Mr. Cavell smiled as he got up and extended his hand to Mr. Peters. "No matter. I'm fond of dogs. I'm glad to see you and your son."

"He doesn't bite, does he, Mr. Peters?" Edith asked. She held out her hand for the dog to sniff.

Before Mr. Peters could say yes or no, the dog gave a stiff-legged bound toward her. Bracing himself against her shoulder, he licked her face. Books, pencils, and pens spilled on the floor as she threw her arms about him.

Everyone laughed.

"Love at first sight, I call it," said Mr. Peters, with a satisfied chuckle.

By now all the children had fallen upon the shepherd and were petting and exclaiming over him. Don wriggled and whined delightedly, beside himself with joy.

"A fine one with children," observed Mr. Peters. "But no good with sheep."

Hal bent over, extracted Don from the muddle, and set him down firmly in front of Edith. "There's your new mistress, Don, my boy," he said. "Now, make a bit of fuss over him," Hal told her. "Then he'll know he belongs to you and you're the one he's to look to when it's time to be fed."

"Oh, Hal!" Edith cried. She patted and stroked the shepherd, calling him, "Good dog, Don. Beautiful dog. Handsome Don." He swelled with pride at her praises.

"Mr. Peters, am I to understand you are giving my daughter this fine sheepdog?" asked Mr. Cavell in astonishment.

"Quite right. Hal and I are making her the gift," declared Mr. Peters.

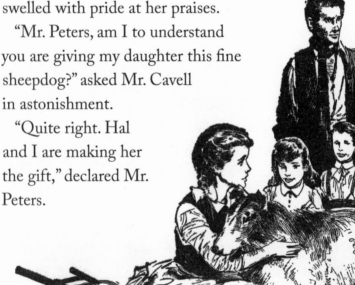

"That's what they told me when they came," confirmed Mrs. Cavell.

"Now, I can't allow you to give Edith a valuable sheepdog," said Mr. Cavell severely. "You and your son are very kind. But one of your sheepdogs! They are priceless to a sheep man, Mr. Peters."

At her father's words, Edith

felt all the joy die inside her. Keeping her arm around Don, she raised pleading eyes to her father.

"Now, Vicar, you let me be judge of that," Mr. Peters suggested. "You know the fine points of religion. But—and no offense meant, mind—you're short on the fine points of dogs."

"No doubt," agreed Mr. Cavell stiffly.

"You see, what my father means, sir," Hal spoke up, "is there are some dogs you can't train to herd sheep. Don's one of them."

"Our dogs have to work," Mr. Peters pointed out sternly. "We've no use at all for a pet dog."

"Like Don, here," went on Hal. "Why, I take him out with a flock of sheep. He minds them for a while. Then off he goes to watch a cart passing on the road. I've given up trying to train him for sheep."

"But, Hal, you're fond of him, so why—" began Mr. Cavell.

"Vicar, we've made up our minds," interrupted Mr. Peters. "Nothing you can say will change it. We brought Don for your daughter, thinking he'd have a good home at the vicarage. We're not going to take him back. You'll have to keep him or find a good home somewhere for him."

"Have to?" Mr. Cavell was indignant.

"Yes. And I might add, Vicar, you're so strict with your children, it is possible you would deny them the pleasure of a pet. The Bishop of Norwich is a good man, but he is not one-half so strict. Come, Hal. We'll be going now."

In the stunned silence that followed, their boots on the bare oak floor sounded like an army marching out the door. Don sprang out of Edith's arms and trotted after them.

Scarcely breathing, Edith waited for something—lightning perhaps—to strike Mr. Peters.

Then she heard her mother saying, "Frederick, you've made Mr. Peters angry, and you've hurt Hal. You cannot let anyone leave the vicarage with hurt and anger in his heart."

"I shall be guilty of false pride if I do," Mr. Cavell accused himself at once. "I must ask their forgiveness and bring them back. Mr. Peters! Hal!" He hurried out into the hall.

"And Frederick," called Mrs. Cavell, "ask them to stay and have lunch with us. It's all ready."

In a moment, Hal strode into the study with Don in his arms. He set the dog down in front of Edith again. "You better keep him on a rope for a few days until he knows this is his home," Hal told her. "If you have a piece of leather, I'll make a collar for him."

Edith's voice trembled slightly with the joy and gratitude she felt. "I think you're the kindest boy in the world, Hal."

Hal set the dog down in front of Edith

Hal's face got bright red. "You probably know no more than a baby about dogs," he said briskly. "So I'd better tell you how to take proper care of Don. What to feed him and so on."

"I am listening," Edith said, smiling up at him gravely.

CHAPTER V

Miss Gibson's School

FROM that day on, Don was considered a member of the family and Edith's special pet. He learned to carry a market basket. When Edith went shopping for her mother, Don trotted proudly beside her, the basket swinging from his mouth.

Each evening when Edith told bedtime stories and drew pictures to amuse Jack and Lilian, Don joined them. Lying on the floor, he dozed with his head on his paws.

Often Edith took care of the neighbors' children while their parents were away for an afternoon or evening. She always took Don with her. While she played the piano and sang to the children, Don sat twitching his ears and staring at her. Suddenly he would begin to howl. This delighted the children.

"Don wants to sing, too," the children said.

And they would all start singing as loud as they could to drown Don's mournful howls. Edith let them be as noisy as they liked for a time. Then quickly she would end the music with a crashing chord and swing round on the piano stool.

Pointing to one of the children, she would cry, "I am a wise bird. I have big eyes that see better at night than in the daylight. What am I?"

When the child guessed "owl," off they all were in a game of "What's My Name?"

Edith was a great favorite among the children of Swardeston. With Don at her side, she and a troop of boys and girls were often seen flying kites, sailing toy boats on the pond, or going nutting in the woods.

On the days when the family had a roast of beef or a big, fat goose, Edith was sure to bring home a ragged, hungry child or two from the poor cottages along the Norwich road.

Time passed. Don became a dignified grown-up dog. He no longer wanted to romp all day long. And Edith was growing into a tall, slender young lady. She no longer wore her hair in braids down her back, but put it up on top of her head. And she went to school instead of being taught at home by her father.

She was a good student. Of the vicar's four children, Edith had the most talent in music and drawing and was most interested in her studies. This pleased her father very much.

The year came when Edith was ready to go away to school to continue her studies. It was decided that she would go to Laurel Court, Miss Margaret Gibson's School for Young Ladies, in Peterborough. This was a town some seventy miles or more from Swardeston.

It was a crisp fall morning when the family saw her off on the train. As usual, Don had come along. He sensed something out of the ordinary was about to happen. And he kept so close to Edith that she could hardly move without tumbling over him.

"Oh dear!" Edith exclaimed. "I wish there wasn't a rule at Miss Gibson's against having pets. I hate to leave Don behind."

"I wish you could take him," Jack said. "He'll miss you terribly."

Down the track, the train whistled for the station.

Lilian thrust a small book at Edith. "If you're going to study French," she said, "you'll need a handy French dictionary."

Her father tucked a small book into her handbag. "To read on the train," he told her. "One of your favorite poets."

"Longfellow?" she said, smiling.

He nodded yes and kissed her quickly on the cheek.

The train roared into the station. Jack picked up Edith's bags and helped her to a seat.

"Look out, Jack!" she cried suddenly. "There's Don."

The dog had followed them into the train. Her brother lifted him in his arms and dashed out. The train began to move. Edith waved to her family. They were all laughing at Jack, who struggled to keep Don from getting away. The two made a funny picture. She was glad to have something to laugh at; otherwise, she would have cried at leaving them all.

Edith opened her book of poems and settled down to read "Hiawatha." It was afternoon when she heard the porter call, "Peterborough."

She stepped out on the platform. An old man in a coachman's hat and long-tailed coat hurried over to her.

Raising his hat, he asked, "Miss Cavell? Miss Edith Cavell?"

When she told him she was, he gathered up her luggage and led her to an ancient but glistening carriage. The fat, sleek horse swung his head around to give her a friendly stare.

It was a delightful drive to Laurel Court that autumn afternoon. The coachman, perched up front, pointed out the sights.

"That old mansion house just over the rise is where we're headed for," he said at last.

As the fat horse traveled at a snail's pace up the rise, Edith looked with interest at the gray walls, shining windows, and many-gabled roof of Laurel Court. Before long she was standing at the door.

At her knock, the door was opened by a pert little maid. "Ah, one of the new ones!" she exclaimed, and ushered Edith into the big hall.

A tall woman in a

black silk dress and stiff white collar came to meet her. She held out her hand to Edith.

"I'm Miss Gibson," she said, "and I know you are Edith Cavell. I've heard your father preach. You look so much like him that anyone would know you for his daughter." She glanced approvingly at the neat appearance Edith made in her broad-brimmed hat, black stockings, high shoes, and tweed coat.

"Most of the young ladies arrived this morning," went on Miss Gibson. "As soon as you have freshened up a bit after your trip, join us in the drawing room for tea."

Edith liked at once the room she had been given. Although it was small, it had a wide, deep window with a beautiful view of the town.

She washed her face and combed her hair. Leaving her unpacking for later, she went downstairs. In the big drawing room, she found twenty or more girls scattered about in small groups, sipping tea, munching sandwiches, and chattering without stopping.

Miss Gibson introduced her to some of them. Then she led her to a circle of girls around a little black-haired, black-eyed woman. The little woman was telling something in French, and the girls were much amused by whatever she was saying, for they were in gales of laughter.

Edith knew a little French grammar and had read a

few stories. But to hear French spoken! The language had a special music of its own. It sang in one's ears. And Edith found the sound fascinating. If she could ever twist her English tongue around the syllables, Edith was determined to learn to speak French.

When the little woman stopped talking, Miss Gibson announced, "A new student, Mademoiselle Valery and young ladies. Edith Cavell."

"Ah!" cried Mademoiselle Valery. "I do hope you are going to like French."

"Oh, I know I will!" Edith told her.

By the time they all left to go to their rooms, Edith felt quite at home and happy among her new companions.

Next morning after breakfast, Edith entered on school life again. She had classes in history and English and took her music lesson before one o'clock. In the afternoon, there was French, drawing, and painting. Then there were games outside.

Often in the evenings there were parties or dances with boys from a nearby school for partners. But school work always came first with Edith. Her father had sent her to Miss Gibson's to learn, and Edith did. Some nights she studied beyond the time to go to bed. And Miss Gibson would tap on her door and say, "Lights out, Edith."

When she wrote home each week, Edith told her family how she was getting along in her different subjects. Usually she had a good report to make.

"But I am happiest about my French," she said in a letter to her father. "I have had nothing but tay-bays in French composition for a whole month. A tay-bay is short for *trés bien*, or very good. It is the highest mark given by Mademoiselle Valery, and she does not give many, so they are much sought after."

Edith enjoyed speaking French so much that she became Mademoiselle's prize student.

"*Bien! Bien!* Good! Good!" the French teacher would exclaim after a lively conversation. "You are *thinking* French words instead of English words. And that is the secret of speaking French."

Sometimes Miss Gibson came in while Edith was reciting. Then Mademoiselle Valery would say, "Edith speaks with a little English accent, I know. But that is not important. What is important—she is using the language like a real Frenchwoman."

For four years Edith remained at Miss Gibson's, spending her summer holidays at home with her family. They were wonderful years, and there was only one great sadness to spoil them. Her beloved dog, Don, died of pneumonia. It happened the last winter she was at school. For days, whenever Edith tried to study, she would begin thinking of the shepherd and all his endearing ways. And the words seemed to swim on the page.

Mr. Peters wrote her from Swardeston. "I am sorry to hear about Don. But he was getting on in years, and maybe it was all for the best. Hal wants me to tell you that we are sure to have another sheepdog who's not fond of tending sheep, and he'll save him for you."

His letter did much to cheer her up.

Then shortly before graduation, something very important happened.

She and Miss Gibson had often talked over what Edith wanted to do after she was graduated.

"I don't know whether I want to teach or not," Edith always told her. "But I do know that I want to work with children."

One day, late in the spring, Miss Gibson called Edith into her office. "I think I have exactly the right position for you," Miss Gibson announced. "A former student of mine married a Belgian lawyer, a Monsieur François of Brussels. She has four children, and she wants an English governess who speaks French well. I thought of you immediately."

Edith's face lighted up. "Miss Gibson! That sounds as if it were made for me! To be with children, to teach them and take care of them—that's what I've always wanted."

"Then I'll write Madame François at once," said Miss Gibson.

CHAPTER VI

Mademoiselle Cavell

ON a morning in September, Edith sat at her dressing table in her rooms in the François home in Brussels. She had never had a real dressing table in all her life. And this one was lovely, as was everything in her sitting room and bedroom.

Edith had arrived in Brussels the evening before. At once she had felt as if she had been dropped into another world. Brussels—the capital of Belgium— was a gay and glittering city. It was completely unlike quiet Swardeston and Peterborough.

Then she had entered the François house. And it seemed to her first, excited gaze that she had stepped into a beautiful painting. Rich rugs lay on the floor of square marble blocks. There were hangings of silk damask. Pictures in gilt frames filled the white walls with color.

While she waited for the servant to announce her arrival, a dainty French poodle came from one of the rooms to stare at her. Edith held out her hand and called softly in French, "Come here, little one."

The dog went to her at once. After a brief sniff, she put her front paws against Edith and stood on her hind legs. As Edith patted her head, four children ran into the room.

"Suzy! Suzy! No, no!" they cried.

"Forgive her, Mademoiselle," the oldest, a girl, begged. "Suzy wishes only to wish you good evening."

"I don't mind your Suzy," Edith said, smiling at them. "I love dogs."

Then Madame and Monsieur François came to meet her. They greeted her warmly and introduced the children.

"This is our oldest, Marguerite, who is twelve," said Madame François. "Then, Jeanne, ten; and Philip, almost nine; and Charles, six."

The girls curtsied, and the boys bowed gravely.

"Mademoiselle Cavell," Charles spoke up quickly, "you do not resemble a dragon at all."

Although his sisters and brother tried to hush him, he continued, "They said you were certain to be a frightful old English dragon. But I think you are very pretty."

The other children denied vigorously that they had said anything of the kind. At any rate, they had not meant it. Marguerite ended the argument at last.

"Obviously," she said in lofty manner, "Mademoiselle is not an old dragon at all. And I am prepared to like her. She might have been another horror like my friend Amie's English governess."

Her parents frowned and shook their heads sadly. But Edith laughed. In spite of their free and easy manners, the children were friendly and lovable. She was prepared to like them, too.

"You may have to turn into a horrible dragon occasionally to manage them," commented Monsieur François wryly.

"Oh, they are mischievous," said his wife, sighing. "You will have to insist that they obey you, Mademoiselle. And they must all learn to speak English. It is so necessary these days."

The children groaned loudly.

"You are not to trouble Mademoiselle Cavell further this evening," ordered Monsieur. And he sent them off upstairs.

Then Madame had called a servant to help Edith unpack and get settled in her rooms. And that had been Edith's introduction to the François family.

Now, as she sat at her dressing table, thinking of the evening before, she became aware suddenly of footsteps, loud whispers, and the rattle of dishes in the hall outside her door. The door swung open. There stood Marguerite with a tray on which was a huge teapot. Behind her were Jeanne and Philip and Charles.

"You are up and dressed already, Mademoiselle!" exclaimed Marguerite in surprise. "It is very early!"

"We wished to bring you tea in bed on your first day," said Jeanne.

"The English must have tea upon waking," Philip declared. "That is what Mama says. She lived in England, you know."

The four came into the room, followed by Suzy. She rushed up to Edith and stood on her hind legs to be petted.

"Suzy wishes good morning, Mademoiselle," explained Charles.

"*Bonjour*, Suzy," Edith said, laughing softly, and scratching the curly back. "*Bonjour, mes enfants.* Good morning, children," she greeted them.

"Clear a table, Philip," commanded Marguerite. "My arms are breaking with this tray."

Philip leaped to remove books and things from a table near a window. Edith felt that a whirlwind had entered her rooms. The children darted about drawing curtains, setting the table, dragging chairs up to it, and talking constantly in French.

"*Merci. Merci beaucoup.* Thank you. Thank you very much," said Edith when they were all clustered about the small table. Even Suzy had managed to squeeze in between Charles and Philip.

"You make me very happy to plan such a nice surprise," Edith told them. She passed the hot rolls around, and each of the children took one.

"We wanted to show you that you had made a very good impression on us last night," Charles explained carefully. "It was Marguerite's idea."

"We all agreed," said Jeanne. She suddenly burst into giggles. "Oh, won't Cook be furious when she finds all the rolls gone!" she cried.

"Didn't Cook give them to you?" asked Edith.

"Ha! Ha! I should say not!" Philip gave a snort. "We have been banished from the kitchen for weeks. Cook calls us pests, getting in her way and always begging for something to eat."

"So one of us goes in and takes things when she's not looking," said Jeanne with satisfaction. "I sneaked the rolls out."

"Then we say we don't know who it was when Cook asks," Charles said. "We won't tell on anybody. It's a pact."

"Oh dear!" Edith sighed. "I think I would enjoy my tea and roll more if Cook had *given* them to you. Now we'll have to tell Cook about taking them and ask if we can't get some more for her."

"We have to do that?" exclaimed Marguerite, astonished. "Why, the rolls are ours. Our father pays for them. It isn't as though we stole—" She stopped quickly as she saw Edith give her a severe look. "It isn't very kind to Cook, is it?" Marguerite said, suddenly humble.

"No, it isn't," agreed Edith quietly.

Philip squirmed in his chair. "I'm not going to tell on Jeanne," he said. "We have to stick to our pact and be loyal and not tell on each other."

"If we all go together, and Jeanne tells Cook about it, we won't be breaking the pact, you see," Edith pointed out.

There was silence for a moment. Then Jeanne said, "I'd just as soon tell as not. I'm not afraid."

Edith smiled. "My, that was delicious tea!" she said. "I don't know when I've enjoyed anything more." She set her cup down. "Come, let us clean up and put the room in order."

No one could have been more amazed than the rosy-cheeked cook when the new governess appeared in the kitchen with the four children. She scowled when she learned about the missing breakfast rolls. But she was so pleased that they were going to the bake shop for more that she hardly scolded them at all for raiding her kitchen.

With a basket on her arm and surrounded by the children and the poodle, Edith set out down the broad, tree-shaded street.

That night she wrote to her family: "You will never believe where I gave my first lesson in English to the François children. It was in a Brussels shop among all the tantalizing odors of spices and fresh bread.

I taught them the English names for the various baked goods. We had a lovely time. And I doubt that they will forget the words they learned. They could see and smell the cake, the cookies, and so on."

Edith also wrote to Miss Gibson. She told her how much she liked the François family and how happy she was in her new position.

As the months passed, she became very fond of the François children and their parents. She was treated like a member of the family, and the children learned to love her dearly. When one of the children was ill, Edith cared for her tenderly until she was well again. They missed her when she went home to Swardeston each summer for a holiday.

Meanwhile, at the vicarage, many changes were taking place. First, Florence left to take a position in London. Then Lilian married a young doctor named Wainright and went to live at Henley-on-Thames. Jack, her little brother, grew up and moved to another town. Only her mother and father were left at home.

Toward the end of her fifth year in Brussels, Edith received sad news from England. Her mother wrote that her father was very ill. When Edith told Madame and Monsieur François about this, they insisted that she get ready to leave for home at once.

With all the François family and their servants, there was quite a crowd in the big hall to bid her goodbye. Suzy, the poodle, sat and watched everything that went on. Edith's luggage made a large pile on the marble floor. Charles looked at it, puzzled.

"Why take so much with you, dear Mademoiselle?" he asked. "You will be back."

"Not for a long time, I'm afraid," Edith replied.

"We shall always expect you," Madame François said.

The children rushed to Edith and threw their arms around her. Suzy jumped up for a last petting. Edith finally broke away and hurried out the door and into the waiting hansom cab. Her eyes were full of tears as she looked back and saw them standing in the wide doorway, waving and blowing kisses.

She waved her handkerchief and called, "*Adieu, mes enfants. Adieu, Suzy! Adieu, mes cher amis!* Goodbye, my children. Goodbye, dear friends."

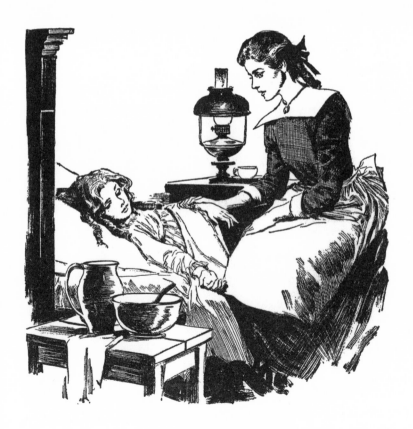

CHAPTER VII

The Watcher

As soon as Edith got home, she rushed up to her father's room. Her mother and the doctor were there. She looked at her father. He lay so very still on the bed that he scarcely seemed to breathe. His dark beard was startling against his thin, white face.

Edith glanced in quick panic at her mother. Mrs. Cavell smiled encouragingly.

"I know it is a shock to you to see your father like this," she said, "but he is better. The doctor says he is going to pull through."

"Yes, the vicar seems to be over the worst," the doctor assured Edith. "The trouble is circulatory. The blood is not circulating properly through the arteries. This affects the supply of blood to the heart. Your father must have rest and quiet. It will take a long time, but I think he will recover."

The vicar opened his eyes. They rested on his daughter. "Edith, my dear," he murmured. "I'm glad you have come home. Don't go away. Stay here at home awhile."

"I won't go away, Papa," Edith promised.

The vicar closed his eyes again and slept.

Edith walked slowly downstairs to the sitting room, where Florence and Lilian and Jack were waiting.

"Papa is going to get well," she told them. "But he needs a great deal of care. Someone has to help Mama. Since Papa wants me to stay, I told him I would."

"But what about the François children?" asked Florence.

"The François children, as you call them," replied Edith with a little smile, "are almost grown. Marguerite is seventeen and will no doubt be married soon. Jeanne is fifteen. Philip is fourteen and going away to school next year. Charles is eleven. He is really the only child left."

"But supposing Papa is sick for a long time," said Jack. "You can't expect the François family to wait for you, can you?"

"I think they would," Edith told him thoughtfully. "I believe I would be welcome there any time. But the truth is, the children no longer really need me. And Papa does. I'll write a letter tonight and explain everything to them."

"Well, I do hope when Papa is well again that you will go on with teaching," Lilian said. "You seem to have a great talent for it. And it shouldn't be wasted."

Edith regarded her younger sister affectionately. "The time will come when I must decide about that," she said. "In the meantime, I'll have to learn how to be useful in a sickroom, if I'm to be of any help here at home."

So after five years in Brussels, Edith came back to Swardeston. She settled in her old room and became her father's nurse.

She fitted into her old life as though she had never

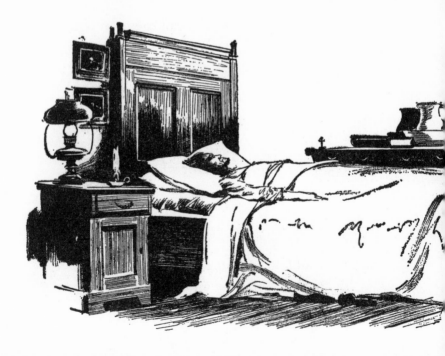

left it. She had enjoyed Brussels and the carefree life
there, with many servants to wait on her, but she
had not been changed. She had been like an English
primrose that grew in strange soil for a time.

Her father got better very slowly. For a long while,
he remained in bed. Edith waited on him and gave
him his medicine. She prepared special food and
coaxed him to eat. He had little appetite, so she took

great pains to make his meals look especially good. When he was restless or felt worse than usual, she sat up beside him at night.

"Perhaps I can go to sleep if you will sing 'Rock of Ages,'" he would say. And in her light, clear voice, she would sing the beloved old hymn.

Sometimes he would wake up suddenly and put out his hand to see if she was sitting in the chair beside the bed.

Finding her there, he would sigh and say contentedly, "Always watching over me." Little by little, he would drift off to sleep again. "Watching. Watching to see that the sick do not slip away forever in their sleep," he would murmur. "Long ago people called a nurse 'the watcher.' How sweet a name—the watcher."

Every day there were visitors who came to see how the vicar was getting along. Mrs. Cavell talked with them about her husband's health and listened to the various remedies they suggested. She allowed some old friends like Mr. Peters and Hal to go up to his room to visit him.

Mr. Peters always said, "You are looking better today, Vicar."

"Much better than the last time we were here," Hal declared at every visit.

They talked about the crops and their sheep. Edith

asked about the dogs, and they told her about each one until she got to know them all by name. When they left, they always promised to come again soon.

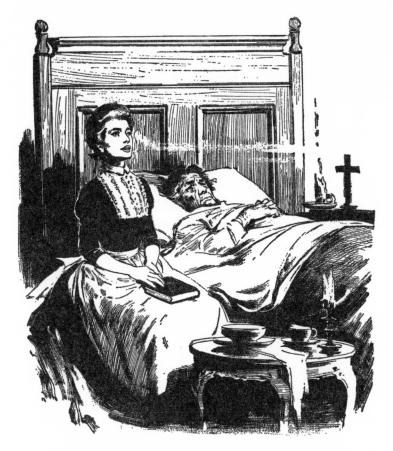

With the vicar sick, many of the parish duties fell to Mrs. Cavell. The sexton and the churchwarden came to talk with her about needed repairs, the church accounts, and arranging treats for the choir and the parish children. She worked, as always, with

the Mothers' Club, which sewed baby clothes, made
flannel blankets, and gave coal and a few shillings
to poor families that were expecting new babies. In
addition, she visited the sick and carried baskets
to the poor. And she made the young parson, who
substituted for Mr. Cavell at Swardeston church, a
welcome guest at the vicarage.

So, with Mrs. Cavell taking care of the house and
parish duties, and Edith nursing her father, the two
managed very well.

The days wore on. At last Mr. Cavell could leave
his bed and sit up. Then he could go downstairs.

It was there before the fire in the sitting room,
almost a year later, that Edith and her father had
a long talk. They were alone, enjoying the warmth
inside with cold rain beating against the window
panes. Edith had put aside her book, for it was growing dark.

"You know, I'll soon be able to go out," her father
said. "But I shall always have to be careful, the doctor
warned me. I must not get too tired. I must not
become worried or excited. Then, too, I am getting
old. It's time to retire."

"Oh, Papa, must you?" asked Edith. "Where will
you and Mama go?"

"There's no need to worry about that," Mr. Cavell
told her. "We'll go to Norwich, where the Bishop

has a place for your mother and me to live. What concerns us is what you are going to do about your work, Edith."

Edith reached out and straightened the shawl which lay over his knees.

"You mustn't worry about me, Papa," she said, picking up some knitting from the table at her side. "While you've been ill, I've had time to do a great deal of thinking. Teaching rich people's children doesn't seem very important to me any longer.

"I want to do some-thing better with my

life. I'd like to help poor people, poor sick people who really need me. These months of taking care of you have made me realize that I want to be a nurse."

"Edith, a nurse?" asked her father in surprise. "Of course, a nurse is a wonderful thing to be. But you are no longer a young girl. A nurse's training is long and difficult. Your days would be filled with hard work and unpleasant duties. Why, you'd have to begin a whole new life."

"Yes, I know," Edith said, smiling at him. "But you taught me not to be afraid of disagreeable tasks and hard work. You see, Papa, *you* taught me to be brave."

Her father looked at her fondly. She was small and slim, but he knew that she was strong and determined. If she had made up her mind to spend her life in taking care of sick people, nothing would stop her.

"Well," he said, "it seems that we are both setting out on new paths. I'm to be a retired vicar, and you are to be a nurse. When do you plan to start your training, Edith?"

"Not until next fall, when you are quite well again," Edith replied. And, laying aside her knitting, she went to help her mother put supper on the table.

CHAPTER VIII

The Probationer

EARLY in the fall of 1896, Edith packed her clothes and a few books in a tin trunk and set out for London to make a second start in life. During the summer, she had applied and been accepted as a student at The London Hospital. She had chosen this hospital because it was in the East End, where the poorest people of the city lived.

When she arrived, the matron in charge of the nurses led her to a small, white room which Edith was to share with three other students. The three were fresh-faced girls from the country. They were used to more space.

"We'll be falling over one another in here, that's certain," said one of the girls.

The matron gave her a bleak smile. "After you are through work here each day, you will need just

enough room to fall into bed at night," she told her
briskly.

"You four have an hour to unpack, get into your
uniforms, and report to the probationers' classroom.
Make sure you are not late."

With that, she left, closing the door on Edith and
her roommates.

While they all chatted, Edith made herself at
home in her little corner of the room. She arranged
her books on a shelf and hung a watercolor of the
vicarage at the head of her bed. She slipped into her
pink uniform.

When all four of the young women were ready,
they walked together in search of their classroom. The
halls reeked of yellow soap, carbolic acid, and cooking
from the basement where meals were prepared. The
four put their handkerchiefs to their noses.

"We'll all get used to the smell, I suppose, and not
notice it all," said Edith in muffled tones.

They came to a door marked *Probationers* and went
inside. Edith found there were a good many students
already there. She and her roommates took seats in
one of the rows of chairs. More girls entered, and
soon the room was almost full.

Edith saw that most of the students were a good
deal younger than she was. They were girls in their
late teens or early twenties. But there were a few

women older than her. At least, Edith thought, there were others who felt that their age should not keep them from going to school to learn.

The matron came in and took her place before the class. She read out their names. Then she made a short speech. She welcomed them, telling them how much trained nurses were needed. Then she spoke of Florence Nightingale, the great English nurse.

"Fifty years ago," she said, "there were no places where women could be trained to become nurses. But through the hard work and devotion of Florence Nightingale, nurses' training is now given in several places.

"It is not an easy training. You will have to learn about diseases, take on unpleasant duties, and do many thankless menial tasks. The work is hard, the hours are long, and the pay is little. But none of this will matter if you have come here to learn to care for the sick because you want to be of greater service to people. To be a nurse will be for you the most important thing in the world."

Edith soon discovered that everything the matron had said was true. The work proved too hard for some. Others dropped out because they could not stand the sight of so much sickness and death. But some, like Edith, stayed on to scrub floors, tend the sick, and study.

There were classes every day. By the time Edith
was in her second year at The London, she had
learned to recognize the symptoms of influenza,
typhoid, and other diseases. She had also learned to
sew up a split finger and to bandage a wound as well
as any doctor. Together with other nurses, she had
watched surgeons operating in what was called the
Operating Theater.

Day after day, she tended patients in the wards
crowded with the sick. In the men's wards, she took
care of longshoremen who had been injured on the
nearby Thames docks, homeless tramps, and feeble,
dirty, old men who had been found wandering in
the streets. She changed their sheets, shook out
their pillows, and arranged their bedclothes. As she
rubbed aching backs, she listened to their complaints
with her cool, still smile.

In the women's wards, there were undernourished
young women with bad coughs and poor, frightened
old women who were not even sure of their own
names. Edith took their temperatures, washed them,
and made them comfortable. She ran endless errands
for their medicines to the dispensary on the ground
floor of the hospital. There the pharmacist mixed
drugs, rolled pills, and made ointments according to
the doctors' prescriptions.

And in the children's wards—here Edith's very

heart melted within her at the sight of them. There
were lame children. There were children who had
been ill-treated and half-starved. There were others
with colds, coughs, and broken bones. Some had
fevers. And there were others who were dying.

As she moved from bed to bed, she put her cool
hand on a hot forehead. A pillow was plumped up. A
rag doll was placed in a little girl's arms. There was
an encouraging smile and a "You are looking better
today," for those who sat up for the first time. For
those who were afraid of thermometers and throat
swabs, she made up beautiful
stories. And the children forgot
their fears.

There were days when the

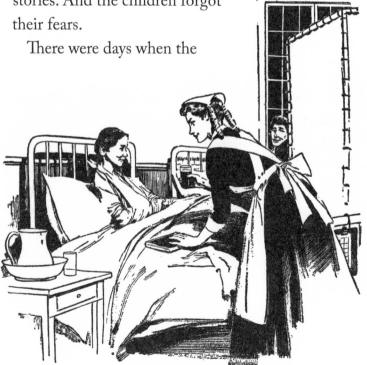

doctors were so rushed they scarcely had time to make their rounds. Catching sight of Edith smoothing down bedclothes and tucking in the children, a doctor would say, "Miss Cavell's mothering will probably do them as much good as any medicine I could give them. She has an odd charm, very grave and kind, that is very attractive."

In a few months, Matron, as everyone at the hospital called her, assigned Edith to the surgical wards. It was an important promotion. Few nurses advanced so rapidly. To be a surgical nurse was to have one of the highest nursing positions.

"I've watched Miss Cavell," said one of the older doctors to Matron. "She has the makings of an unusually fine nurse. But do you think she's quite ready to work in surgery?"

"If anyone is, she is," replied Matron. "She's quick, deft, and very clean. She knows what to do and does it without becoming ruffled. She is always calm and serene."

Edith would have been surprised to hear Matron say that. She knew she did not always feel calm and serene. Sometimes she could not speak because she was afraid her voice would tremble. Many times she wanted to cry, but she held the tears back!

The doctor understood this. "Calm and serene, Matron?" he said with a laugh. "I would say that

Miss Cavell was always thoughtful, gentle, and
encouraging. At any rate, I'll be willing to try her in
surgery."

CHAPTER IX

Nurse Cavell

EDITH straightened her cap as she hurried down the long corridor of The London Hospital. On reaching the children's ward, she stopped beside the bed of a little boy whose head was swathed in bandages. When she saw that he was sleeping quietly, she smiled.

"He'll be all right now," she thought with relief, and she turned to one of the other small patients.

Several weeks had passed since she had been assigned to the surgical wards. She had learned to dress wounds, to take out stitches, and to work with the surgeons.

Because she was so quick and skillful, the surgeons often asked for Nurse Cavell when they had to perform difficult operations or care for people who had been very badly injured. They knew that they could depend on her to assist them calmly and efficiently.

Now, as Edith left the children's ward, a young probationer stopped her in the hall.

"I've been looking all over for you," she said. "Matron wants you in her office right away."

Wondering what the matron wanted, Edith hurried to the office. Matron looked up from some work on her desk with a worried frown.

"We have just heard that there is a terrible epidemic of typhoid fever in Maidstone, about forty miles from here," she told Edith. "The town can't handle all the cases, and they have asked the hospitals in London to help.

"I am putting you in charge of a group of nurses to go to Maidstone at once. I don't know what your relief group will be asked to do. The epidemic struck suddenly, and there has been no time to get organized. So you may have to make your own decision as to how your nurses can be of most help." She handed Edith a list. "Here are the names of the five who are to go with you."

Edith glanced down the list. "I know them all," she said. "I'll get them together, and we should be ready to leave in an hour."

With their black medical bags and a few clothes, Edith and her five young women reached Maidstone early in the afternoon.

"Have you seen much typhoid?" was the first question Edith was asked by the doctor who was head of the town's hospital.

"Yes," answered Edith. "We have frequent cases of it at The London."

"Then you'll do," grunted the doctor. He led them into a room in which beds had been placed so close together that there was hardly space to walk between them. On the beds lay the sick, with dry, feverish faces. Their wasted bodies were covered with rose-colored spots.

"We received our first typhoid fever case in the morning four days ago," related the doctor. "By evening there were eight. In two days every bed in the ward was filled. By the third day, there were two hundred cases. Today all the hospitals are filled. We are forced to turn cases away. We have nowhere to put another man, woman, or child," he finished in despair.

"Then if it is agreeable to you," Edith suggested, "my nurses and I will act as visiting nurses. We will care for the sick in their homes."

"That would be the greatest help you could give us now," the doctor said gratefully. His face was gray from having worked for days with almost no sleep.

One of the offices was cleared, and some cots were set up for the nurses to sleep on. Edith was given a list of people who had developed typhoid but had not received medical care. Using a map of Maidstone, she marked the addresses of these typhoid cases. Then she assigned a special area to each nurse. Before sending them out to the homes, Edith told them:

"We know that typhoid fever is caused from drinking impure water and eating impure food. But we know as yet of no remedy for the disease. All we really know is that absolute cleanliness is necessary. The water must be boiled before drinking. The food must be pure. You must make every well member of

the family realize this. As to nursing the patient..."
Edith paused and looked round the circle of earnest
young women.

"I can add nothing to what you already know," she
said. "All of you have taken care of typhoid cases at
The London. Because so little is known as yet about
treatment for the disease, we must expect that a good
many of our patients will die, in spite of all we can
do. Your greatest task will be to prevent more people
getting the disease."

She picked up the list of those she was going to
visit herself. "I think we should get started," she said.
"Report back here at eight. We'll compare notes and
plan the next schedule."

That was the beginning of weeks of work during
which Edith and her nurses scarcely dared stop to eat
or rest. They walked through deserted streets where,
in almost every house, people were ill with typhoid.
They climbed stairs to find whole families lying ill.

Cheerfully, the nurses bathed patients, took
temperatures, felt pulses, changed bedding, prepared
food. They cleaned up and disinfected sickrooms.
And they taught as much home care as they could to
those who were well.

"You and your nurses are doing outstanding work,
Miss Cavell," the head of the Maidstone hospital
told Edith when she met him coming in one evening.

"Except that you look as if you haven't slept for days, I would not know you are helping to handle an epidemic. You have been of the greatest help to us in nursing the sick and in keeping the epidemic from spreading. I shall write to the head physician and the matron at The London and tell them so."

The doctor was as good as his word, and news of Edith's fine work at Maidstone spread to other hospitals. Before long, she left The London, since she had been asked to become Night Superintendent of a smaller hospital near by. Then she was appointed Assistant Matron in a larger hospital. And at last she was asked to serve as Matron of the Ashton New Road District Home in Manchester during the absence of the regular matron.

Matron! Nurse Edith Cavell had now reached the top of her profession.

Edith said goodbye to her many friends in London before she left.

"Be sure to take plenty of warm clothes," Matron at The London Hospital cautioned her. "Manchester is one of the coldest places in England."

Edith was glad she had taken Matron's suggestion when she arrived in Manchester on a gray, raw day. She needed the extra warmth of the woolen shawl she wore under her cloak as she rode in a dilapidated cab through the city to the nursing home.

Edith had thought that London was smoky and sooty. But Manchester was worse by far. It was an important center for iron and coal mining and for the manufacture of pottery, ironware, and cloth. Smoke from the mills, the potteries, and the collieries enclosed the city like a fog.

The Ashton New Road District Home was a small hospital in an old building at one end of Grey Mare Lane. Years of soot and grime had darkened the walls inside and out. To Edith, it was like coming out of a big modern house into an old-fashioned cottage. A doctor, a matron, and some nurses not only tended patients in the hospital, but they also went out on sick calls.

The doctor was a little man with a face as brown and wrinkled as an English walnut. He seemed to think that London's big hospitals spoiled nurses for a place like Ashton. But Edith quickly proved to him that she could not only teach and supervise the nurses, she could also work harder and longer than any one of them.

Although she often had to make many sick calls after her other work was done, she always managed them all. Armed with her black bag and with her great cloak flying in the wind, she hurried through the streets of Manchester and in and out of the houses of the sick.

Many times during the course of her daily round, she heard someone call out, "There goes Nurse Cavell!" and a girl or boy would come running up to her to ask her to see an old grandfather or grandmother. Or a youngster would say, "Please, Nurse, my dad asks if you can stop a minute. He's got the rheumatism in his back again."

And she never refused to squeeze in that extra visit.

Many people in Manchester worked under bad conditions in the mills and mines and factories. And they lived in crowded, unsanitary homes.

So there was much sickness.

And no week passed

without its accidents to workers in the mines and factories.

Edith saw to it that there was always clothing for the new babies in families too poor to provide it. She saw to it that no sick call was not answered promptly. And from the supplies at the Home, she lent everything from bedding and furniture to hot water bottles and clean nightgowns.

"Return it clean and in good condition," she told the borrowers. If they did, they could have almost anything.

The poor of Manchester looked upon her as their own Florence Nightingale. "Nurse Cavell never turned anyone down who really needed help," they said.

One bitterly cold day, Edith made a call on a patient who lived not far from the coal mines. As she was leaving the house, she heard a great noise. It was almost like a clap of thunder. There came another and another. Almost at once, she saw women and children and men pouring out of the houses and running down the road in the direction of the mines.

A man passed her. "Explosion in the mines!" he shouted at her and sped on.

"Explosion!" Edith, her heart thumping at her throat, rushed down the road after him.

A whistle blew in sharp and piercing blasts, giving

the alarm. It was like a terrible voice from the clouds, calling for help.

Edith saw the crowd gathered at the scene. They were unnaturally quiet. A rescue squad disappeared into the mine shaft. The crowd of women and children and men watched the mine entrance with horrible fascination.

Before long, blanketed bodies began to be brought up out of the shaft.

Edith pushed her way through the crowd. As the injured miners were laid on the ground, she examined them. One man was dead, cut to pieces by the explosion. Another had a bad head wound. Bind it up, stop the blood from flowing. Stitch it later. Be careful with that one with the broken leg. Don't move that one, his back seems broken.

She moved quickly from one to another, giving first aid. The miners' wives helped her, asking what to do if they did not know. Children brought blankets, clean rags for bandages, and hot tea and coffee. The men rigged up stretchers.

"Would you hurry and bring the doctor and some nurses from the Home?" Edith asked a man.

"The whistle will fetch them quick enough," he answered. "They can hear it at the Home, and they always send help."

Under Edith's direction an emergency field

hospital was set up, with the wounded wrapped in blankets and laid on the ground in orderly rows. She had the men carry the worst cases on stretchers to the nearest house, to get them out of the bitter cold.

By the time the doctor and several nurses from

the Home reached the mine, she had the relief well organized. Soon other nurses and doctors arrived. Edith pointed out the injured who needed immediate attention. And they all set to work.

Darkness came, and they worked by lantern light as more and more injured were rescued from the mine. The miners who were hurt badly were given first aid and sent to the Home and other hospitals. Those with slight wounds were given first aid and sent home. Weeping families walked to their homes beside stretchers bearing the miners who had died.

Toward morning, snow began to fall. It covered

the three wounded who were still left lying on the ground, wrapped in blankets. The white mounds looked like graves. Edith felt herself trembling with fatigue and with the horrors of the past night.

She looked around. She and the three wounded were alone. All the others, like giant shadows in the yellow glow of the lanterns, stood at the mouth of the mine. The rescue squad was still digging in the mine, searching for two miners still unaccounted for.

Edith looked down at the grave-like mounds. She knew none of the men had been too badly hurt to be taken home by their families. Then why were they lying there? "They have no families, no one who cares whether they live or die," she thought suddenly.

Then she noticed a little black dog sitting beside one of the wounded miners. He must have slipped past her while her attention was on the group at the mine entrance. She went over and bent down. The dog whimpered, then barked as she touched the man's face.

An arm moved beneath the blanket, and a hand came out to pat the dog.

"Ah, Blackie!" the miner cried softly. "You found me at last."

The dog licked his face.

"None of that now," the man scolded him fondly. Then looking up into Edith's face, he explained, "You see, Blackie waits for me near the mine entrance, and we walk home together to the boarding house every evening." He turned to the dog. "You must have waited for me for a long time in the cold this night, Blackie."

"We're going to take you to the hospital," Edith said, tucking the man's arm under the blanket.

"You're not going to leave Blackie!" he cried, trying to raise himself.

"There, there," Edith soothed him. "Of course not. Blackie's going along, too. Now, just lie back quietly."

Edith walked quickly over to the group at the mine entrance and spoke to the Home's doctor. "There are three men left back there," she said. "I think we ought to get them to the hospital as soon as possible."

"By all means," replied the doctor. "One of the men here has a horse and wagon. He'll take you. And take the nurses with you. They won't be needed here any longer. I'll stand by. The rescue squad is still trying to dig out the two men believed to be missing. But there's little hope that any buried in the rubble all this time will be alive."

The man with the horse and wagon brought them round, and the three wounded miners were laid carefully on the straw on the wagon bed. Blackie barked furiously. He jumped and growled at the men when they picked up his master.

"What a horrid little black dog!" exclaimed a nurse. "Go away!" she ordered him.

"Blackie is not horrid," Edith told her. "He's guarding his master." She spoke soothingly to Blackie. In soft, gentle tones she lured him to her, and he let her pick him up. A minute later she was on the wagon seat with Blackie on her lap.

The nurses let down the tail gate and sat with their feet swinging off the back. The driver slapped the reins. Weary and shivering, Edith and her nurses rode back to the Home in the snowy morning.

Once there, the other nurses at the Home took over while Edith and her group washed and changed their clothes.

Before sitting down to the hot breakfast the cook had prepared, Edith took Blackie into the kitchen for his meal.

"We have a house guest," Edith told the cook, with a smile. "Blackie's staying here until his master gets well."

"I'll enjoy having a dog about the place," the cook said. "Always had a dog or two on the farm where I grew up. Now, you just leave him to me, Matron Cavell; I will take care of him. And you go eat your breakfast."

Edith thanked her and started to leave.

"Oh, Matron," the cook called. "Everyone was rushing around taking care of the wounded, so I took in the mail yesterday. There's a letter that perhaps you ought to see at once. It's foreign and looks important. I left it on top of the pile on your desk."

"Foreign?" It probably was from Marguerite François. "Only she is not Marguerite François any longer," Edith thought as she hurried to her office.

"She is Madame Pierre Graux. I keep forgetting that little Marguerite is now a married woman."

She picked up the letter. It was from Brussels. But it was certainly not Marguerite's handwriting. Or, for that matter, the writing of anyone in the François family. She looked at the name in the return address—Dr. Antoine Depage. She knew no Dr. Depage. Edith slit the envelope with her paper knife and took out the letter.

CHAPTER X

E. Cavell, Directrice

AFTER breakfast, with the letter in her hand, Edith went to talk with the little doctor.

"I have good news," she told him, her gray eyes shining. "A Dr. Depage wants to open a nurses' school in Brussels, since there are none in all of Belgium. He already has four brownstone houses which can be used for the school. But he needs someone to organize the school and to direct it. And he wants *me* to be that person."

"Huh!" said the little doctor grumpily. "I don't see why you should want to go to Brussels. How did this Dr. Depage hear about you?"

"Through a friend, Marguerite François Graux. Her mother-in-law is one of the sponsors of the school."

"Are you going to take the position?" asked the little doctor.

Edith nodded. "Oh, yes. Your regular matron will be back soon. And this is exactly the kind of work I've always wanted to do."

That very evening she wrote Dr. Depage, accepting the position. His reply arrived shortly: "Come at once."

Many people in Manchester were deeply sorry to see "Nurse Cavell" leave. At the Home, even the little doctor told her, "We shall miss you more than I can say."

Edith flew around to get ready. Within a few hours she was on her way to Norwich to say goodbye to her parents. The next day she was crossing the English Channel on her way to Belgium.

When she arrived in Brussels, everything seemed to move much faster than it had when she was there twelve years before. Of course, it was 1907 now. Electricity, telephones, the automobile, and other inventions of modern science had brought changes to this ancient city.

Edith had no trouble finding Dr. Antoine Depage's offices. When she entered the reception room, she saw two women, one middle-aged and the other young, in a corner, knitting. The younger woman got up, rushed at Edith, and threw her arms about her.

"Oh, Mademoiselle! Mademoiselle!" she cried.

"Marguerite!" Edith exclaimed with delight. "What a lovely surprise to find you here!"

Eagerly Marguerite introduced her mother-in-law and then Madame Depage, who appeared in the doorway of her husband's office. Next Dr. Depage himself came to greet his new *directrice*. And soon all four were on their way to see the new school.

The four houses which were to be used for the school and for a private hospital were on Rue de la Culture, in a suburb of Brussels. Two of the houses, No. 143 and No. 145, contained rooms for patients. No. 147 and No. 149 were given over to the Directrice, her nurses, her students, and the servants.

L'École Belge pour les Infirmières Diplomées was the name given to the school. Few were ever to call it by that name, however. It became simply the Clinique to most. And some, later, referred to it as the Edith Cavell Clinique.

When the school opened, Edith had exactly four students—three Swiss girls and one Belgian. And she had two supervisors, English nurses who spoke not a word of French.

"But six are at least a beginning," Edith thought. "There might have been none at all."

Edith had already designed a uniform for the probationers—blue cotton dress, white collar and long cuffs, white apron with bib, and white, stringless caps. The probationers arrived at their first class in their new uniforms. Sitting as stiff as four china dolls, they drank in every word of Edith's lecture.

"Always remember you are a member of the nursing profession and entitled to respect," she told them soberly. "You address the physician as Doctor. He addresses you as Nurse. He gives his orders in a professional manner, not as though he were ordering some menial about."

She stopped speaking, startled by a giggle which was quickly smothered. It came from the plump, blond Belgian.

"Mademoiselle," Edith said sternly, "perhaps if you tell us the joke, we can all laugh."

After much stammering, the Belgian girl told her that doctors would think it silly to say Nurse this and Nurse that. They had always treated nurses like servants, and they always would.

"Even doctors can learn good manners," Edith pointed out crisply.

"But Madame la Directrice," began the Belgian, "you don't understand. In Belgium, nursing is not considered respectable enough for nice young ladies. Of course, if one is a nun, that is different. Nuns have always tended the sick."

The three Swiss girls agreed that many parents in Brussels did not want their daughters to be nurses.

Unfortunately, this was true all over Belgium and in other European countries.

Edith knew she would have to spread the news widely about the new school and advertise for students. She wrote articles about the school and about nursing for medical journals and various magazines. She advertised for nurses in the newspapers of other countries. And she had posters made which said in big letters: GIRLS WANTED TO TRAIN AS NURSES.

People all over Brussels cooperated and pasted the posters on the outside of their buildings.

In no time there were thirteen students at the Clinique. But as yet, there were no patients.

One sunny Saturday, Edith sat in her bare little room, when she heard dogs fighting in the street. Looking out, she saw a bull terrier and a thin, shabby cur in a fierce battle in front of No. 149. The cur was fighting wildly but with great courage. Then quickly the bull terrier darted in and sank his teeth in the cur's throat.

Grabbing the pitcher of water from her commode, Edith ran out. The shabby dog lay bleeding and gasping. She flung the cold water at the bull terrier. He yelped in surprise and sprang away. With a growl at Edith, he trotted off down the street. Picking the wounded dog up in her arms, Edith carried him inside.

The noise of the fight had brought students running into the hall. They had called their Directrice "Madame" from the first day of school. Now they asked, "What are you going to do with the poor dog, Madame?"

"I am going to take care of his wounds. Then I am going to give him a bath and a meal," replied Edith.

She smiled round at them, then announced, "Students, the Clinique has at last received its first patient."

Four years later, the dog, named Don for her childhood pet, was still at the Clinique. And Edith had another pet—a sheepdog called Jack, which Mr. Peters had given her when she had visited her parents in Norwich.

During those four years, the Clinique had grown tremendously. Now there were sixty-two nurses in training. They came from many countries—Germany, France, England, Holland, Switzerland, and Belgium itself.

The nurses' sitting rooms rang with their songs and laughter. Once in a while, after the evening class— during which some were so tired that they could scarcely keep awake—Edith would play to them on the ancient, out-of-tune piano.

Not only had the number of students grown, but so had the staff. And Edith now had an assistant— an English nurse named Elizabeth Wilkins.

Miss Wilkins was badly needed, for Edith was busy from morning till night. She barely had time to bathe her two dogs, which she tried to keep almost as clean as her patients. And although she went to the theater once in a while, she had hardly a minute to call her own.

As the months sped by, she was asked to supervise

three other hospitals in Brussels, in addition to the
Clinique. She trained scores of nurses. She wrote
many articles on nursing. And she superintended the
care of hundreds of patients.

Late at night when it was quiet, she usually went
over the bills and accounts of the Clinique. There
was never enough money. Sometimes there was
scarcely enough to buy food for the nurses, let alone
pay them. Often it seemed to Edith that one diffi-
culty followed right on the heels of another.

"If I could not spend some time with my youngest
patients now and then, I don't know what I would

do," Edith said one day. She was speaking to Miss Wilkins who had just come into her office.

"I'm going to have that drab brown nursery over at St. Gilles hospital painted a pretty blue and white," she went on. "We'll put some pictures on the walls, too. Maybe we can even get a piano someday, so that I can play to the children."

"Play to the children, with all you have to do!" snapped Elizabeth Wilkins. "It's no wonder you look so tired. Well, I'm tired, too. I've come to tell you that I've been offered a position as supervisor of another hospital, and I intend to take it."

"Oh, no," began Edith. But Miss Wilkins went right on.

"There can't possibly be harder work anywhere in the world than there is here," she added crossly. "And if I go, at least I'll be rid of all the waifs and strays you keep bringing into the Clinique."

"Waifs and strays!" Edith said in surprise. "You surely can't be talking about José. The Clinique rings with his praises. He helps out our maid, does odd jobs, runs errands." José was an orphan Armenian boy whom Edith had found at one of the city hospitals not long before.

"I wasn't thinking of José at all," said Miss Wilkins.

"And Don, poor dog, is gone now," continued Edith. "Of course, there's Jack, but he's no stray. So that leaves Pauline. She's the only other waif I can think of at the moment."

The summer before, on a vacation in Norwich, Edith had found fifteen-year-old Pauline Randell abandoned by her parents. Since then she acted as a second mother to the girl.

"Do you mean Pauline?" asked Edith. "Has she been annoying you in some way?"

"Oh, no," said Miss Wilkins wearily. "I don't know how we got off the subject. I just came here to tell you that I'm leaving the Clinique."

Edith looked at her thoughtfully. The young woman had worked until she was little more than skin and bones. She seemed ready to weep from fatigue.

"What you need is a rest," Edith told her quietly. "Take a month's vacation in Switzerland, Elizabeth. I can get the money for you somehow. After that, perhaps you'll think differently about leaving us."

Miss Wilkins managed a little smile. "I feel differently already," she said. "Now that I stop to think about it, I know I'd never be really happy working anywhere but here."

She left the office, closing the door gently behind her. Edith sank back in her chair. Suddenly she, too, felt dead tired. She was glad that it would soon be time for her own vacation. She planned to spend it with her mother, who was alone now, for Edith's father had died four years earlier.

Glancing at the calendar on her desk, Edith read the date—June 14, 1914. "Exactly a month from now," she thought, "Pauline and I will be on our way to Norwich."

CHAPTER XI

At the Seashore

A FEW days later, Edith was teaching a class in anatomy. The blackboard was covered with her drawings of the bone structure of the body—backbone, legs, arms, joints. The students sketched busily and made notes. They always enjoyed any lecture which Madame illustrated.

"She makes everything so clear," the students said. "Of course, Madame is a marvelous teacher."

The period was half over when Pauline, her pert nose in the air, came tripping into the classroom. She begged pardon very primly for the interruption. Then she said to Edith, "Dr. Depage asks if you will please come at once to the office."

"Oh dear!" Edith sighed. Something most unusual must have happened to make him interrupt a class. Excusing herself, she went downstairs.

Both the doctor and his wife were there. They were as excited as two children.

"*Les nouvelles sont bonnes!* Good news!" cried Madame Depage, the moment Edith entered the office.

"We are going to have the school!" exclaimed Dr. Depage. "Yes, Madame la Directrice, we are going to have the new school at Uccle. Work will start on it any day."

For a long time, a new school building had been badly needed. The committee of sponsors had agreed. A location in Uccle, a mile south of the Clinique, had been found. Plans had been drawn. Now work on the new building was to begin.

It was wonderful news. On returning to her class, Edith spent the rest of the period telling her students about the modern nurses' training school which was to be built.

Just before luncheon, she picked up the noon edition of the afternoon paper to glance through the news. On the first page was the story of a double murder. Archduke Francis Ferdinand, heir to the Austrian throne, had been assassinated the day before, Sunday morning, June 28, 1914, in Sarajevo. His wife also had been killed.

Edith had never heard of Sarajevo. From the story, she gathered that it was a village in the Balkans.

Ferdinand, the Crown Prince of Austria, was only a name to her.

She read the papers carefully afterwards, but there was little mention of the murder. Soon the whole thing seemed forgotten.

The fourteenth of July came, and Edith and Pauline went off to England. Edith found her mother had aged a great deal, although she was gay and sprightly. They decided to take a place at Yarmouth, the famous seaside resort not far away.

Soon Edith's brother, Jack, and her sisters, Florence and Lilian, joined them.

"It's good to see all my children together," Mrs. Cavell said contentedly. "I so seldom do. We are scattered these days. Edith in Brussels, Florence is superintendent of a hospital in London, Jack miles away from Norwich, and Lilian at Henley-on-Thames."

The days went by—long, pleasant days. There were picnics on the sand. In the evenings they watched scores of big and little fishing boats put into the great harbor with the day's catch. At night as they all sat out under the stars, they could hear the music from a dancing pavilion down the beach.

But this happy time was soon to be over.

One hot morning toward the end of July, Edith and Pauline were returning from a walk on the beach. Edith stopped at a newsstand to buy a paper. She

unfolded it. There in great black letters were frightening words:

AUSTRIA DECLARES WAR

Austria had declared war on Serbia, July 28. The
Serbian terrorist who had killed the Austrian Crown
Prince and his wife in Sarajevo had let loose all the
pent-up hatred and conflicts between Austria and
Serbia. And they had exploded into a war.

"Oh, they are always fighting about something in
the Balkans," Jack said, when Edith hurried back
with the news.

"I think this is much more serious than just another Balkan quarrel," Edith told him. "I think it may mean trouble for other countries, too."

The next day, the Austrians shelled the Balkan city of Belgrade. It was like the first roll of thunder on a sunny day. Quickly the storm clouds of war began to gather as one nation after another began to take sides with Austria or with Serbia.

Now many people were beginning to be really alarmed. Newspapers were snatched up the minute they appeared on the stands. In the sitting room of the house at Yarmouth, the Cavells gathered to discuss the news. Although Edith seemed very calm, she was greatly disturbed.

"I must return to Brussels at once," she told her family.

"But why?" asked Lilian in a worried voice. "You are English, Edith. If this war spreads, you will be better off in your own country than in Belgium."

"The war *is* spreading," Edith insisted. "And that's why I must go. If there should be fighting in Belgium, our nurses at the Clinique must be ready to care for the wounded. I must pack at once and leave for Belgium as soon as possible."

She started for her room. The others followed, protesting that she must not go—that there would be nursing for her to do in England, if England

should fight, and she would be safer, if she would
only stay home.

At last Pauline burst into tears. "Don't go away
and leave me!" She clung to Edith's hand. "If you are
going, I want to go with you," she wept. "I can't bear
it, if you don't take me. Please, take me with you."

"Very well," Edith said, rolling up a pair of black
stockings and tucking them into their suitcase. "Pack
your things carefully. We must get everything into
a few bags. Boats and trains are sure to be crowded.
Thousands of summer tourists will be rushing home
to their own countries. There is really no telling what
the traveling will be like."

Later that day, the family went with Edith and
Pauline to the railroad station. The station was filled
with incoming vacationers who had little thought of
war. Pushing their way through the crowd, Edith and
Pauline climbed aboard a waiting train and found
seats. As the train pulled away from the station,
Edith peered through the dusty window.

There on the platform stood her mother, wiping
away tears and leaning on Jack's arm. Florence and
Lilian stood close beside them. Edith tapped on
the window to attract their attention. Then, forcing
herself to smile at them, she waved until they were
out of sight. She never saw their beloved faces again.

CHAPTER XII

War

As Edith and Pauline journeyed to Brussels, war crept closer. On August 1, Germany, an ally of Austria, declared war against Russia, Serbia's friend. France was Russia's ally. So, on August 3, Germany declared war on France. And she demanded the right to send troops across Belgium to attack France. Belgium refused and sent troops to the borders to keep the Germans out.

Now boats, trains, and stations were jammed with people seeking safety. Achingly tired from the boat trip across the English Channel and from riding in a packed train, Edith and Pauline arrived at the Clinique on August 3.

José, the young Armenian, met them at the door. "Oh, Madame, I'm glad you're back!" he cried.

Edith's shepherd, Jack, bounded into the hall,

wagging his tail in welcome. Elizabeth Wilkins and a whole group of nurses came rushing out.

"Thank heaven, you are safe!" they exclaimed.

"We've been hearing all kinds of frightening rumors about the Germans," announced Miss Wilkins as José began to carry in the bags. "All our patients have fled in panic to the coast."

"All of them?" asked Edith.

"Yes, Madame, all," answered a pretty young nurse named Jacqueline Van Til. "Even the two who had to be carried to their cars on stretchers."

"The best thing for us to do then," said Edith at once, in her quiet, practical tone, "is to get the empty rooms ready for new patients."

Now that Madame had taken matters over in her confident way, the nurses felt better. They went to work in a burst of energy.

Edith had not been back very long when she was called to the telephone.

"Edith!" It was the voice of Madame Depage. "I'm so glad you're back safely. I'm speaking from the palace, here in Brussels."

"The palace!" Edith was surprised.

"Yes. King Albert and Queen Elisabeth have turned part of the palace into a Red Cross hospital, and I am in charge. Our friends, the Graux, and other families are turning their homes into hospitals, too."

"And where is Dr. Depage?" asked Edith.

"He's in charge of a hospital near the French border. French troops are massing there, ready to fight the Germans. The news is bad, Edith."

Indeed, the news was very bad, and it rapidly grew worse. At eleven o'clock the next morning, the German army marched into Belgium. At four o'clock, the Belgians and Germans were fighting.

If the Germans invaded Belgium, England had promised to go to Belgium's aid. England now declared war on Germany. The First World War had begun.

Edith sent some of her nurses to the other hospitals where wounded soldiers had begun to arrive. And once more she hurried through the streets with Jack at her heels, on her daily round of duties at the hospitals of St. Gilles, St. Pierre, and St. Jean.

Meanwhile, although the Belgians fought bravely, the German army advanced steadily toward Brussels. The people in the capital waited tensely as, day after day, the enemy drew nearer.

On August 19, Edith left the hospital of St. Jean to return to the Clinique. Coming along a road into the city, she saw crowds of people. Some were on foot with bags and bundles on their backs. Some rode on a pile of household goods in carts pulled by a worn-out horse. Others walked beside little carts drawn by great Belgian dogs.

A boy with one of the dog carts shouted at Edith,
"*Les Allemands sont là!* The Germans are coming!"

They were refugees fleeing before the advance of
the German army.

That night everyone at the Clinique went up to
the roof. From there they watched the sky light up
with the glare of rockets and saw the smoke rise
from a battle going on only a few miles away. The

roar was deafening. Pauline, José, and the dog, Jack, huddled close to Edith. About them clustered the nurses. Some of them began to cry.

"I'm afraid," Jacqueline wept. "I have talked with refugees. They tell awful things about the Germans."

Edith took Jacqueline's trembling hands in her own. "We mustn't be afraid, my child," Edith said. "Nurses must think of the sick children, of the women, the wounded men. We mustn't consider ourselves. Our place is with the suffering. Besides, the Germans are not going to harm nurses. Their soldiers will need nursing when they are wounded, just the same as other men."

Jacqueline choked back her sobs, and the other nurses felt comforted. Next day, they stood in the hot sun and watched the long, green-gray lines of German soldiers marching into Brussels, hour upon endless hour.

"Remember," Edith told them as they sat in their basement dining room at dinner, "the Germans are now in control of the city. We must not show our resentment against them. And we must treat their wounded as well as we would treat our own."

When she finished speaking, Jacqueline Van Til laid down her fork and covered her ears. Cannons had begun to boom in the distance. She wondered how Madame could remain so calm.

With thousands of the German soldiers in the city,

Brussels soon looked like a German military camp. The smoke from their outdoor cookstoves rose from the Grande Place. The streets rang with the tread of their hobnailed boots.

Posters with new German regulations and the punishments for not obeying them appeared daily on walls and billboards. One poster announced that no one was allowed to read newspapers unless the papers were printed by the Germans.

Another poster forbade Belgians to ride bicycles. Germans had discovered that boys on bicycles were carrying messages to the Belgian army. Still another poster forbade Belgians to keep pigeons. Pigeons carried messages, too.

But the Germans had not forbidden the people of Brussels to visit one another. Often Madame Depage left the Red Cross hospital at the palace and went to the Clinique. There she and Edith discussed the war work which they and their friends were doing.

One September day, after terrible fighting near the Marne River in France, Madame Depage asked, "Edith, have you heard what the Princess de Croy and her brother are doing?"

The two women were sitting in Edith's office. Leaning forward in her chair, Marie Depage lowered her voice.

"They have turned their beautiful chateau in the

Mormal Forest into a hospital and—" Her soft voice grew even softer, "they are doing something far braver than that. A young school teacher—Louise Thuliez—brings them wounded English and French soldiers. She finds them in shell holes, barns, deserted houses, in the woods—wherever they can hide from the Germans. The Princess keeps them there until they are well enough to be moved, and then—"

She glanced at the door to make sure it was shut. "Then," she went on, "she and her brother, with the help of a man named Hermann Capiau, get them over the border into Holland or France where they will be safe."

Edith nodded knowingly. She herself had already managed to spirit two or three wounded soldiers out of Brussels, right under the noses of the German police.

"If the Germans should ever find out—" she began. Then she stopped suddenly as someone knocked on the door.

It was Pauline with a message, and nothing more was said that day about the chateau in the forest. However, Edith was not surprised when a man came to see her sometime later and told her he was Hermann Capiau. He was a short man, with brilliant blue eyes and bristly hair.

"You know of our work with refugees, I believe," he said.

Edith nodded, "Yes, Marie Depage has told me."

"Then, perhaps, you will help us," he said. "There are two wounded English soldiers hidden outside the city. I fear the Germans may find them."

"Then I fear they will be shot," said Edith. "Only a few days ago, I heard that the Germans shot thirteen Allied soldiers whom they found hiding in a barn."

"Will you take these men into the Clinique?" asked Monsieur Capiau.

"Yes," Edith answered. "They will be safe here. To everyone they will be patients, that's all."

At seven o'clock, a few evenings later, Edith was having supper with her nurses as usual. Marie, their little maid, entered, looking rather frightened, and went over to her.

"There are two strange men outside. They are hurt."

"Thank you," Edith said. Getting up from the table, she followed Marie to the door.

In the light streaming from the hall, Edith saw two haggard young men standing on the doorstep. Their dirty and bloodstained clothes hung in rags. The older man had his arm around the younger to keep him from falling.

Edith reached out and helped them inside.

CHAPTER XIII

The Secret of No. 149

WITH José's help, Edith got the two wounded men to her private office.

"We are very grateful to you," the older man said in English to Edith. "We realize the risk you are taking."

"You are my own countrymen," Edith told him. "In times like these, there is a higher duty than prudence."

She went out. In a few minutes, she returned with Jacqueline Van Til, who stared in amazement at the two sick, ragged men.

"Take the young man who is too ill to speak and whose name is Pierre," directed Edith, "to Room 9. The other young man, whose name is Louis, is to be put in Room 12. I will send Nurse Paula van Bockstaele to him."

Jacqueline noticed how pale and anxious Madame's face was, but she said nothing. She helped Pierre to his feet. Then with Louis following them slowly, she half-led, half-carried her patient to his room.

Jacqueline removed his tattered shirt to dress the wound in his shoulder. For a second, she could not imagine what he had wrapped about his chest. Then she recognized the English flag. He was an English soldier! Across her mind flashed the words of the poster plastered on walls all over Brussels:

"Any male or female who hides an English or a French soldier in his house shall be severely punished."

Jacqueline made herself forget her fright and take care of her patient.

Later that night, Jacqueline and Paula told the other nurses about the two English soldiers. At first they were all very worried. It was dangerous to break the Germans' rule. But without a doubt, Madame had taken the Englishmen into the Clinique to save their lives. They could trust their directrice always to do what she knew in her heart to be right.

Next morning when Edith went to visit the two patients, she saw Jack lying in the hall between the two rooms.

"Guarding our friends, aren't you?" she said, patting the dog.

Edith found the men much better. By the end of the week, they were well enough to leave the Clinique. Edith had been told what to do by Hermann Capiau.

"Wake your patients at four o'clock tomorrow morning," she told Jacqueline and Paula. "Tell them to be ready to leave."

To José, she said, "Have bread and hot coffee ready. And put ten slices of bread in a bag for each of the men."

It was still dark the next morning when Edith got up and dressed. The two soldiers, in Belgian working men's clothes, were waiting with José downstairs. Edith opened the front door and looked up and down the street to see that there were no German patrols in sight.

"Come, José," she said. "You walk with me. The men will follow at a safe distance."

They all set out through the quiet suburb. Walking just as if she were answering an emergency sick call, Edith led the group to a house in the Avenue Molière. The owner, a former patient of hers, would see that the soldiers got safely across the border into Holland.

By seven o'clock, Edith was back in her office at the Clinique, and José was busy washing windows.

The next afternoon, in the bright sunlight and

under the very noses of the Germans, the young
schoolteacher, Louise Thuliez, arrived at the Clinique
with eight English soldiers and one Frenchman.
Edith asked Jacqueline to see that rooms, baths, and
food were prepared for the hungry, worn-out men.

Then before dawn, a few days later, Edith and José,
with Jack trotting beside them, led the men to the
outskirts of the city. There a young Belgian by the
name of Gilles, that met them to guide the men out
of Belgium.

There were constant comings and goings of English and French soldiers now at the Clinique. Edith grew thin and haggard from her many after-midnight journeys.

"Madame, where are all these soldiers coming from?" Jacqueline asked Edith one day. "Only a few are wounded. Most of them are just half-starved and worn out from walking a long way."

Knowing that Jacqueline could be trusted, Edith told her quietly about the work which Louise Thuliez and the Princess de Croy were doing.

"There are now several people who hide these soldiers and help them escape to Holland," she added. "One is Monsieur Capiau, whom you have seen here. Another is a man named Philippe Baucq, who lives not far away. And there is a young man named Gilles who leads escaping soldiers across the Dutch border. But you must not mention these names to anyone, my child."

"No, Madame," Jacqueline promised soberly. "I will remember."

All through the fall and into the winter, groups of soldiers continued to arrive at the Clinique. Some came now without having to be guided. "Edith Cavell Clinique, Number 149 Rue de la Culture," were the magic words whispered to a soldier trying to escape from the Germans.

Edith took them all in. The Clinique was always full. As fast as she could spirit several away, more appeared to take their places.

Edith seemed so unconcerned about danger, everyone felt quite safe at the Clinique. There was even an air of gaiety about the place. Some of the soldiers got into the habit of dropping into the little Café Chez Jules down the street for a glass of red wine in the evening. They passed the time talking or playing dominoes with the men and their wives who came there regularly.

"Word is getting around Brussels that you are hiding English and French soldiers," Monsieur Capiau warned Edith. "You should not allow the men to go to Chez Jules. People are bound to be suspicious."

"People who go to Chez Jules are Belgians," Edith said. "They live around here. They would never tell the Germans anything."

"But you must realize that the city is full of German spies," Monsieur Capiau said, his temper rising. "A spy might drop in at the café anytime. The men should be kept inside the Clinique."

"They are not animals," Edith retorted. "I cannot cage them."

Christmas, 1914, came. Edith let an English officer at the Clinique give a party for fifty poor Belgian children. For hours, No. 149 rang with happy voices.

Just before midnight, they all sang England's "God Save the King." It was forbidden to sing the national anthems or even folksongs of any country except Germany. But those in Edith Cavell's Clinique felt quite safe.

The Germans had never shown the slightest interest in the Clinique. Furthermore, they had not once interfered with the building of the new school in Uccle. Edith went regularly to see it. She often took some of the nurses with her. In January, the workmen were telling them, "It will be ready for you to move into in another six or seven months."

Meanwhile, life in Brussels was becoming more and more difficult. Houses were cold, for the Germans had taken all the coal. There was almost no gas or electricity. Oil for lamps was scarce. But worst of all was the threat of starvation. No crops could be raised in the war-torn land. And there was scarcely any food left in Belgium. Yet somehow the Belgians managed to get through the winter.

Spring came, and Madame Depage arrived at the Clinique one day to tell Edith that she was going to the United States to ask the Americans to send money and help to the Belgian hospitals. At the same time, the well-known American, Mr. Herbert Hoover, was working to organize a committee for the relief of Belgium and France.

And in Brussels, people were turning every empty lot into a potato patch. Opposite the Clinique were several empty lots where, in June, men and women of the neighborhood worked planting rows of potatoes.

Sometimes they could hear the piano and men's voices singing gaily: "It's a long way to Tipperary. It's a long way to go."

And the potato planters would look across at the Clinique. They knew the words. Some Belgian printers had defied the Germans and printed the rollicking English soldiers' song.

"I am sure some of these gardeners are spies," Jacqueline declared to Edith. "I saw one of them watching the Clinique the other day, listening to the men sing 'Tipperary.' He looked very suspicious."

"You are beginning to see German spies everywhere," Edith said. "You are as bad as Monsieur Capiau." She put a gentle hand on the nurse's shoulder. "Come, how would you like to walk over to Uccle with me to see the new school? It will be finished in August, and you haven't been over there yet to select your own room."

"I would like to go very much," Jacqueline answered. She regarded Edith fondly. Madame was as pale and thin as a ghost, she thought worriedly. "But Madame, why don't you lie down and rest?" she said. "You look so tired. We can go another day."

"I haven't time to rest now," Edith said. "There are too many things to be done. Besides, the walk will do both of us good." She called Jack, and the three started out.

They had a very enjoyable tour of the school. Jacqueline could not get over how very big and grand it was. *"C'est magnifique!* It is magnificent!" she kept exclaiming.

They walked past the potato patch on the way back. Edith stopped to chat with some of the workers. Jack stretched out on the grass beside the walk. Jacqueline went on across the street to the Clinique.

In a few minutes, Edith heard Jack growl. She turned and saw a well-dressed handsome man approaching. He apologized in French for bothering her.

"I am looking for the Edith Cavell Clinique," he said. "My friend and I are running from the Germans. My name is George Gaston Quien, and I am a French soldier. My friend, Mr. X, we'll call him, is English. We must find a place to hide as soon as possible. I have been told that the Clinique is in the Rue de la Culture, and that it is a safe place."

His eyes wandered casually over the people in the potato patch, now busy with their hoes. Then he glanced over at the Café Chez Jules.

"Where is your friend?" asked Edith.

"He is waiting around the corner," replied
Monsieur Quien.

"If you will bring him—" began Edith.

The man was off before Edith could finish.

"Hush, Jack," Edith commanded her dog. He was
growling threateningly.

Quien returned with Mr. X, who at once greeted
Edith in English. "We have been having a pretty
rough time of it with the Germans," he said. "I hope
you can help us."

"Come with me," Edith said and led them across the street and into the Clinique.

Next day, Gilles guided Mr. X and several other men to the Dutch border. But Monsieur Quien stayed at the Clinique, saying he was too sick to travel.

When Gilles returned, he warned Edith, "I think that Mr. X is a German spy."

Jacqueline Van Til and Elizabeth Wilkins thought that Monsieur Quien might be a spy also. They were glad when he left three weeks later, with Monsieur Baucq, who was taking another group of escaping soldiers to Holland.

Monsieur Baucq was suspicious of Quien, too. As soon as he returned to Brussels, he went straight to the Clinique and into Edith's office.

"Your Quien may say he is French," he announced, closing the door behind him, "but he is spying for the Germans. It is no longer any secret to our enemy that Number 149 Rue de la Culture is a hideout for English and French soldiers."

Edith looked at him as though she had not heard one word. Her face was paler than ever and very sad.

"You know, Monsieur Baucq," she said, in a voice choked with tears, "two German soldiers were here earlier. They brought me a letter which stated that my dear friend, Marie Depage, went down with the

British liner, *Lusitania*. She was on her way back to Belgium when the ship was sunk by a German U-boat."

Monsieur Baucq got up and went quietly out of the office. Edith needed to be alone with her grief.

CHAPTER XIV

Arrest

AFTER Gilles' and Baucq's warnings, Edith was never sure, from hour to hour, but that the German police would come to search the Clinique. Yet she never let her nurses know that she was worried. She carried on her duties exactly as before. And she began to make arrangements for moving into the new school.

"We have no money for new furniture," she told the nurses, "but the old will do, if we give it a fresh coat of paint."

José brought buckets of paint from the store down the street. Everyone set to work.

No police came to the Clinique. Edith noticed, however, some laborers repairing the street out front. They did little work. Hour upon hour, they leaned on their picks and shovels and gazed at the Clinique.

There were no soldiers hiding inside, and no new ones arrived. So there was no immediate cause for alarm.

Then, one July afternoon, the Princess de Croy came all the way from her chateau in the forest to have tea with Edith.

"Louise Thuliez has found thirty more soldiers," said the Princess. "I cannot keep them at my place. The Germans watch it constantly. Could you take those soldiers here, Edith?"

"The Clinique is no longer safe," Edith told her sadly. "Those workmen out front watch everything that goes on here."

But the Princess begged so hard that Edith agreed to take in the men, a few at a time. About a week later, the first group of nine English soldiers slipped into No. 149.

Edith put them in a room on the ground floor at the back of the house. It had a door which led to the garden.

She asked José to see that the men had something to eat, then went into her office to plan how to get the soldiers to safe hiding places. Glancing out the window, she saw that the workers were no longer in the street. That was strange. She shook off her feeling of uneasiness and began to work.

The nurses and servants were stirring about, taking down curtains, packing books and china in barrels.

Edith had been at her desk for some time when she heard the doorbell ring. In a moment, it rang again.

"Everyone is probably busy in another part of the house," Edith thought. She hurried to the door and opened it. On the steps stood two German officers and two German police inspectors.

Edith caught her breath. The long-expected visit from the Germans had finally come. All the same, the appearance of the four men was so sudden that she was shocked and frightened. She quickly stifled her fear. It would be dangerous to seem in the least alarmed.

"Yes, gentlemen?" she said calmly, looking at them with polite interest.

"We would like to speak with Miss Cavell, the directrice," one of the officers said in English.

"I am Miss Cavell," Edith replied. "Won't you come in?"

The two officers stepped inside. The two policemen stationed themselves on each side of the entrance. As she led the officers to her office, Edith listened for sounds of the soldiers in the room down the hall. She could hear nothing but José and the nurses hammering packing crates. She left the door of her office open, praying that one of the nurses would see the Germans and warn everyone.

"We are looking for some Allied soldiers, reported to be hiding in this neighborhood," the English-speaking officer told Edith. He gave her a keen look. Edith met his eyes coolly. "It will be necessary for us to search this place," he declared.

"Yes, of course," she agreed.

Her casual tone seemed to puzzle the Germans. Their spies had informed them that the Clinique was a regular hideout for French and English soldiers. Edith's calm manner almost made them doubt their spies.

"You will find the place quite upset," Edith told them politely. "We are packing, getting ready to move to our new school in Uccle. No doubt, you know about it."

"We have seen it," replied the officer stiffly. He darted an angry glance at her. It was awkward to be treated as if they had dropped in for tea. "Come," he said to his companion.

The two hurried out of the office. Edith heard them call in the two police inspectors to help with the search. Then she sat listening as they went through the house, opening closets and cupboards. Bang, clatter, tramp—in and out of the rooms, up and down stairs. As the search continued without success, Edith knew that her loyal nurses must have acted quickly.

When she went to the room at the back of the house, the only trace of the soldiers was an English cap. The Germans had seen it, she supposed. But the cap was no good to them without the man who wore it.

She was still in the back room when she saw the four Germans returning. They seemed at a loss. It was clear that they had not found anyone who did not belong in the Clinique. They stood in the hall looking vaguely around for a bit. Then with sudden purpose, they marched into her office.

They began slamming things about. There was the crash of glass, the crack of wood. The failure of their search had made them feel vengeful. They were truly tearing her office apart to find records or letters to prove that the Clinique was a hideout. But in a short time, they gave that up, too.

Three of them stamped out of the Clinique, leaving one of the police inspectors on guard in the front room.

Edith slowly climbed the stairs to her bedroom. Jack came loping after her and flopped down outside. Feeling faint and dizzy, she sank to the floor beside the bed and pressed her face into her hands. A little prayer she used to say when she was a child came to mind. And she repeated in a low voice the simple, trusting words. Gradually, her thoughts drifted back to her childhood in Swardeston.

It had been many months since she had heard from anyone at home. And she never knew whether or not the letters that she sent ever reached England.

When the faintness left and she felt better, she rose and went downstairs. Jack followed her. It seemed these days that he could not bear to leave her side.

At the foot of the stairs, she almost ran into Elizabeth Wilkins.

"I was just going up to fetch you," Elizabeth said cheerfully enough. "Tea is ready in the dining room."

"Excellent," Edith said. "I'm quite hungry."

She took her place at the head of the table. She glanced round at the anxious faces of her nurses.

"My dears," Edith said fondly, "don't be frightened any more. All of you acted so promptly and bravely, the danger is past for now. That police inspector will get tired of waiting for something to happen and will leave before morning."

Edith's confident words loosened their tongues. And they told her all about how they had spirited the soldiers away. Pauline had seen the Germans when they first came in, and she had run to tell the nurses.

While some of the nurses held the Germans in useless conversation, others had sneaked the nine Englishmen out the door to the garden. The men climbed the stone wall and disappeared into the backyard of the vacant house next to No. 149. The nurses began to feel quite cocky over outwitting the Germans.

"I took two of the men across town," Pauline said proudly. "They will be leaving on a bus for Holland. It's all arranged."

By morning, as Edith had predicted, the

policeman was gone. The Clinique sank back into the quiet life of the Rue de la Culture. But to Edith, it seemed that all was too quiet. Rumors and the echoes of rumors reached her ears. The Germans were making arrests all over Brussels. She heard that Baucq, then Louise Thuliez, then the Princess de Croy had been arrested. The rumors grew louder and more menacing all the time. They began to have a fearful sound, as of a storm about to break.

On August 5, 1915, José, Pauline, and several nurses finished piling furniture into a light wagon in front of the house. They had borrowed the wagon from the stable around the corner, to take the last few loads of household goods to the new school.

José went off with the wagon, and the women returned to the Clinique. They were in the hall talking when they were alarmed by a great shadow in the open doorway. Looking more closely, they saw three large men blocking the entrance.

"We understand you are selling some of your old furniture," one of the men said.

"Yes, we have a few pieces for sale," Elizabeth Wilkins replied.

"We would like to see them," the man said, advancing into the hall. With that he whipped out a revolver.

"Madame! Madame!" Elizabeth screamed at the

top of her lungs. "Run, Madame, run! It's the secret police!" She whirled and started toward the stairway.

"None of that!" the man ordered. He reached out and, grabbing her arm, shoved her into the front room. "The rest of you get in there. Line up against the wall," he commanded, waving his revolver at them.

Crying, "They're coming! They're coming for you, Madame!" Pauline raced upstairs.

"*Eine kleine mädchen.* A little girl," one of the Germans said. "Let her go."

A car roared down the street and stopped in front of the Clinique. While the man with the revolver stood guard over the nurses, his companions climbed the stairs in search of Edith.

Awakened by the cries and screams, Jack, who had been asleep in the garden, rushed into the house. Barking loudly, he sprang up the steps after the men.

Edith was not in her office. She had gone across the hall into a little serving pantry to put some fresh water in a vase of roses. She looked up quickly when she heard the commotion in the hall below, the tramp of men's feet on the stairs, and Jack's barking. Then, the next moment, Pauline, the dog, and the two Germans burst in upon her.

Pauline flung her arms about Edith, sobbing with fright and shock. The policemen dragged her back. The vase fell and smashed. The roses lay strewn on the floor and were trod upon in the scuffle. Jack barked and leaped at the men.

"Quiet, Jack! Down!" Edith commanded.

"You are under arrest, Madame!" announced one of the secret police in a loud voice. "Come with us."

His companion gave Edith a little push into the hall.

It had all happened so quickly that Edith was scarcely aware of the excited pounding of her heart.

She felt numb as she walked down the stairs with
the two policemen behind her, and Pauline and Jack
behind them.

Seeing the nurses cowering in the front room,
Edith stopped.

"Don't be so sad, my children," she told them.
"Everything will be all right. I'll be back soon."

She walked out the door and into the police car
waiting at the curb. She could hear Jack howling
dismally because she had not taken him with her.

As she was driven away, she saw Pauline running
after the car like some wild, distracted creature.

"Don't leave me! Don't go away and leave me!" the
girl cried.

It was like the echo of Pauline's cry that summer
day in Yarmouth before the war began. And it filled
Edith with deep sadness. Was it only a little over a
year ago? Oh, what a long time ago it seemed!

CHAPTER XV

Prisoner

THERE was a weary time of waiting, as in the heart of action there always is. And there was stillness. In cell No. 23 in the prison of St. Gilles, Edith could have heard a spider weave its web. She had been kept in solitary confinement ever since her arrest more than a month before.

As soon as she had been allowed to write, she had sent a letter to one of her patients:

"I do hope you are not worrying about me. Tell everybody that I am quite all right here. I suppose from what I hear that I shall be questioned one of these days. Then I shall know what they mean to do about me.

"Is Jackie sad? Tell him I will be back soon. Remember me to the nurses and household.

"I am afraid you will not be able to come and see

me at present. But you can write, only your letter
will be read by the prison censor."

The censor read Edith's letter. There was nothing
in it that he could object to, so he sent it on. Soon
after, she began to receive a packet of food each
Sunday and letters from her beloved nurses. They
told her they had moved into the new school.

"It is all very different from our old
home," they wrote. "Jack cannot get
used to it and keeps returning to the
Clinique. Pauline or José have to go
and bring him back."

This past week, Edith had received

a bouquet of her favorite flowers from "her children." She knew how they must have scraped to get together enough copper *sous* to buy them. She wrote to thank them.

Her letter brought courage and hope to the nurses who waited so anxiously at the new school. When José gave the letter to Elizabeth Wilkins, they gathered around her in the sitting room, and Elizabeth read the letter aloud:

"My dear Nurses:

Your beautiful flowers brought life and gay colors into my cell. The roses are still very fresh. But the chrysanthemums did not like prison life.

"It seems from your letters that the new clinique is very nicely arranged. I hope I will see it soon and all my nurses as well. ...."

"Of course Madame will see it soon," one of the nurses exclaimed, when Elizabeth Wilkins had finished reading the letter. "Surely the Germans won't keep her much longer."

"She's done nothing worse than to hide Englishmen and Frenchmen and sometimes a Belgian and help them escape," Pauline spoke up. "Lots of people have done that."

"Oh, the Germans will punish her in some way, of course," another nurse said. "But it's not as though she were a spy. We will soon have her with us again."

"But why will they let no one see her?" Elizabeth Wilkins said with a troubled frown. "It must be dreadful, all alone like that, with time passing and probably nobody telling her anything." She rose quickly from her chair. "I am going to the prison and try again to be admitted," she declared.

Elizabeth Wilkins was denied permission to see Edith that day. But several days later, the prison authorities did allow her to visit Edith in her cell for a few minutes.

When Elizabeth returned to the new school, the nurses could see she had been crying. "What is it?" they asked anxiously. "Is she very unhappy? Is she ill?"

Elizabeth removed her long nurse's cape, flung it over a chair, and sat down wearily.

"She's grown very pale and thin," Elizabeth reported. "She sews and embroiders and reads her prayerbook. But the light is bad. There is only one window in her cell, high and very narrow."

The nurse sighed and passed a hand across her forehead. "I am afraid Madame is beginning to lose hope," she told the others. "As I was leaving, she said to me, 'I have done what was my duty. The Germans must do with me as they will.'"

More dreary days went by while Edith waited, uncertain. The Germans still had not told her of what she was being accused. "Arrested and held on suspicion" was as much as she could learn. Of what they were suspicious, they never really said.

Then, on a day early in October, the door of Edith's cell opened and a prison matron came in.

"You must get dressed," she told Edith, not unkindly. "Your trial is to start this morning."

"Where will the trial be held?" Edith asked quietly.

"In the Senate Chamber of the Parliament House," the matron told her.

Edith got up and dressed. She put on the drab dark-blue prison dress and combed her hair neatly. When she was in her hat and coat, the matron led her through the echoing stone corridors of the prison to the entrance.

The bright sunlight dazzled Edith after so many weeks of confinement in her cell. When her eyes became accustomed to the light, she gasped at what she saw.

Over thirty persons were lined up in front of waiting buses. They were guarded by German soldiers in spiked helmets. Among the prisoners were many faces Edith recognized—Princess de Croy, Louise Thuliez, Philippe Baucq, Hermann Capiau, and others.

They were herded briskly into the buses and driven through the streets of Brussels to the Parliament Building. Then they were conducted between lines of German Military Police to the Senate Chamber, where the trial was to be held.

The galleries overlooking the large room were crowded with German officers. Some of them carried field glasses through which they studied the prisoners curiously.

Edith and the other thirty-four prisoners were given seats in the middle of the room. Guards were stationed between each one so that they could not talk to each other.

The lawyers entered and took their places. Then five judges, dressed in magnificent uniforms and each

wearing the Iron Cross of Germany, came in and were seated. The court was called to order, and the trial got underway. Each prisoner answered as his or her name was called from a list.

The thirty-five were accused of having worked together to aid British, French, and other Allied soldiers to escape.

Then one of the officers read from a book of military laws: "Whoever, with the intention of helping the enemy or of injuring the German troops, is found guilty of this crime will be sentenced to death for treason."

There was a muffled scream. Then absolute silence.

"Edith Cavell!"

Edith stood up. Her cheeks were pale, her lips ashy, but she stood stiffly erect before the German officers.

The questioning began.

Was it not true that she had received English soldiers at the Clinique? That she had nursed them and given them money and food?

"Yes, it is true," replied Edith.

Did she deny that she knew these soldiers were going to try to cross the border into Holland?

"I do not deny it," said Edith.

Had she any reason for helping them?

"They were English, and I am English," Edith answered. "I wanted to help my own countrymen."

Had she helped as many as twenty soldiers?

"More than twenty," Edith replied. "Two hundred."

"You were foolish to help your countrymen,"

remarked one of the judges. "The English are notoriously ungrateful."

"On the contrary," Edith told him with spirit, "they are most grateful."

"How do you know that?" he asked, giving her an odd, dry little smile.

"Because," she answered, "some of them have written to me from England to thank me."

"Ah, so they have written to you from England!" cried the officer. He glanced round triumphantly at the other judges. This woman dared to admit that she had helped Germany's enemy! She knew that the English soldiers she helped to escape would return to fight the Germans!

For two days, Edith and the other thirty-four people were questioned by the German officer judges. Some of the people became hysterical with fear and could not answer. Others, like Baucq, became enraged by the nagging questions and shouted wildly at the judges. Some of the men and women told lies. Others told only a little part of the truth. Several turned on each other in a bitter quarrel.

But Edith had learned as a little girl to hate lying. And now, even though she was in great danger of her life, she clung to the truth.

The German officers as well as her friends, Capiau, Baucq, Louise Thuliez, and the Princess, were puzzled. They could hardly believe that she was not frightened. They did not seem to understand that she was only very determined to tell the exact truth. Once or twice she even corrected the judges when they made a mistake about the time and the number of soldiers that Gilles had led to Holland.

The judges resented, more than the Belgians and the French, this one Englishwoman in her drab prison dress who told the truth with simple dignity. It galled them to hear her tell with patriotic pride of nursing back to health wounded English soldiers.

She looked so thin and frail that she might break as easily as an eggshell. Yet, by her own admission, she had helped two hundred soldiers escape from the Germans! She was head of the Clinique, which was the very center of the activities of the whole group! A little middle-aged woman like that!

Edith's lawyer got up to defend her. She had never seen him. And she could not see him now, because he sat far back in the courtroom with the other lawyers.

"It was all done because of her love for humanity," Edith heard him tell the judges. "She opened the Clinique to the soldiers of every nation. She nursed Germans as well as other soldiers."

The judges scarcely listened to the lawyer. The Englishwoman had admitted her guilt. She refused to say anything in her own defense. Therefore, she must be punished as a traitor.

At the end of the second day in court, the officer who was conducting the trial stood up. Facing the five judges, he said:

"We have considered the cases of the accused, and we are of the opinion that the following persons are the chief organizers in aiding the escape of English, French, and Belgian soldiers."

Edith sat very still, perfectly still, looking straight at the German officer. Her heart seemed to stand still, too, as he began to read the names: "Philippe Baucq, Louise Thuliez, Edith Cavell..."

The trial was over. The prisoners had been found guilty of high treason. Now the judges would decide what their punishment would be.

But Edith was not yet to know what would happen to her. It was not until three days later that she found out. About four o'clock on a Monday afternoon, the door of her cell was opened. A guard stood there.

"Fraulein," he said, "you are to come with me."

As the guard hurried Edith down the echoing corridor, she saw the others who had been on trial with her. They, too, were being marched by guards to the large assembly hall of the prison.

When all thirty-five of the prisoners were

gathered in the hall, the officer who had conducted the trial entered. An aide handed him a long sheet of paper on which were listed the names of the prisoners and the punishments which had been decided upon. In a loud voice, he read off the list to the silent group.

As from a long way off, Edith heard him thunder: "Edith Cavell—*Todesstrafe!* Death!"

CHAPTER XVI

The Dark Hours

EVER since she was a little girl, Edith had prepared herself to meet all kinds of troubles. In her life as a nurse, she had seen much suffering. She had been in close touch with death. She was not afraid to die.

Soon after she was brought back to her cell from the assembly hall, the officer and his aide came to her. They told her that she was to be shot as a traitor at dawn of the following day. Edith remained perfectly calm and steady as she heard the news.

There were last letters to be written to her family and to her "dear children," the nurses. It was the letter to the nurses that took the longest time. From a great crowd of thoughts, she had to choose a few.

"It is a very sad moment for me," she began, "when I write to say my goodbyes to you."

She told of how the Clinique had started, had grown, and how, "in your beautiful new house," the nurses would have more patients and all that was necessary for everyone's comfort.

Edith ended by saying, "If there is one among you whom I have wronged, I beg you to forgive me. I have been perhaps too severe sometimes, but never voluntarily unjust. And I have loved you all much more than you thought.

"My best wishes for the happiness of all my girls, those who have left the school, as well as those who are there still. And thank you for the kindness you have always shown me.

"Your devoted directrice,
Edith Cavell."

Thus Edith came through the dark hours to the night before she was to die. She had been told the final hour would be seven o'clock in the morning, and she knew that she would be taken from the prison earlier. She had never seen the sort of firing squad that was to end her life. But from a deep inner peace, she could think about it now without fear. That she would face the guns quietly and bravely was her great hope.

Putting on her wool dressing gown—for it was cold in the stone prison—she sat down to read her Bible.

Meanwhile, at the Clinique, a smuggled message

had come from the prison. The Germans wished to keep the execution of Edith Cavell secret until after her death. But the father of one of the nurses had found out about the death sentence and sent word to Elizabeth Wilkins. The nurses heard the dreadful news in stunned silence.

"It is impossible!" cried Jacqueline. "We have asked about Madame several times a day at the prison and at the American Legation. The Americans are taking a special interest in Madame's case. Every time, we have been told there is no news."

"We must do something to stop it!" Elizabeth Wilkins declared. She ran to get her cape, and with another nurse, Beatrice Smith, hastened through the rain to the prison of St. Gilles. There they asked to see the Deputy Governor of the prison, who was a Belgian.

He nodded his head sadly when they asked him if what they had heard was true.

"But we *must* stop the execution," Elizabeth Wilkins cried. "Tell us what we should do."

"You had better go to the American Embassy," the Deputy Governor said. "You alone can do nothing."

As the two nurses left the prison, Elizabeth Wilkins said, "We'll go to Monsieur de Leval. He is connected with the American Legation. Perhaps he can help us."

Monsieur de Leval was amazed at the nurses' news.

Only an hour before, he had been told by German officials that no sentence had been decided on for Edith Cavell. But with Elizabeth Wilkins and Nurse Smith, he hastened to the American Embassy.

There they learned that the Reverend Stirling Gahan, Edith's minister, had been told to visit her in the prison that night. It was true. Both Edith and Philippe Baucq were to be shot in the morning.

Elizabeth Wilkins sank into a chair, and tears came to her eyes. Up to now, she had been hoping that there was a terrible mistake somewhere. But there was no mistake.

Monsieur de Leval came over and spoke to her gently. "Why don't you take off that wet cloak, Nurse Wilkins, and try to rest a bit? You've been on the go ever since four o'clock this afternoon, and you've had no dinner."

"Dinner!" Elizabeth Wilkins exclaimed. "Monsieur de Leval, don't you realize it is nearly ten o'clock now? The time is running out."

"I know," he said soberly. "But we will not give up. The American Minister, Mr. Brand Whitlock, is ill. But he is writing a letter to the Political Governor of Brussels. Mr. Hugh Gibson, the Secretary, and I will take it to the Governor, Baron von der Lancken. Wait for us here."

With Monsieur de Leval and Mr. Gibson went

the Spanish Minister, the Marquis de Villalobar. The three men took the Legation car and roared off in search of the German Political Governor.

The Baron was at the theater that rainy evening. Hugh Gibson sent an orderly to tell him that they were waiting to see him at his home on a matter of greatest importance. The Baron would not leave the play until it was finished, and it was half past ten by the time he arrived home. When he had read Brand Whitlock's letter, he shrugged helplessly.

"Only von Sauberzweig, the Military Governor, can stop the execution," he explained. "He is the highest authority in this matter."

"Then telephone him!" they all urged.

"But he's in bed by this time," said von der Lancken.

"Then get him out of bed," demanded Villalobar, Spain's representative. "It's a woman's life that is at stake. You can't shoot a woman like that!"

"I'll see what I can do," said the Baron, and he went into his office to telephone the Military Governor. In less than half an hour he was back. "It is useless," he reported breathlessly. "Military Governor von Sauberzweig told me that the execution was decided upon. And he cannot change that decision. No one, the Governor told me flatly, can do anything for you—not even the Emperor of Germany, Kaiser Wilhelm himself."

"It is idiotic, this thing you are going to do!" cried
Villalobar.

The Baron did not deny that it was, but he could
do nothing to prevent it.

It was well after midnight when the three men
returned to the American Embassy. Elizabeth
Wilkins and some of the other nurses, who had
joined her in the reception room to wait, did not
need to be told that the men had failed. Sadly, the
nurses made their way down the steps and out to the
dark, rainy street. Hardly a word was spoken as they
walked back to the new Clinique, to which Edith
now would never come.

In her prison cell, Edith lay resting on her cot.
Earlier in the evening, the Reverend Gahan, her
pastor, had visited her. Sitting in the flickering
candlelight, they had talked quietly for a while. The
ten weeks in prison had been a period of rest in her
always hurried life, Edith told him. The guard and
jailers had all been very kind and thoughtful.

Edith and her pastor recited one of her father's
favorite hymns together:

> "Abide with me! Fast falls the eventide;
> The darkness deepens: Lord, with me abide!
> When other helpers fail, and comforts flee,
> Help of the helpless, O abide with me!"

Reverend Gahan's good, kind face was sorrowful

as he paused in the doorway on leaving. "This is the first time I have been allowed to see you. They have even refused to let me be with you at the end," he said sadly.

Edith told him that he should not grieve for her. She was glad to die for her country.

Then she said, "Standing as I do, in view of God and eternity, I realize that patriotism is not enough. I must have no hatred and no bitterness toward anyone."

At five o'clock, Edith rose and dressed in the drab prison dress. She made her bed as neatly as she had

ever made a hospital bed. And back at the Clinique, Elizabeth Wilkins, unable to sleep, got up, too. She dressed quickly and went to the prison and stood by the entrance.

When the guards came at six o'clock, Edith was waiting. She had just finished making a note in her prayerbook:

> Died at 7 a.m. on Oct. 12th, 1915
> With love to my mother
> E. Cavell

Placing the book in her pocket, she walked, with head held high, down the passage between the two armed guards and out to the courtyard.

The rain was over. In the pale dawn, two gray cars waited. In one, Philippe Baucq already sat between his guards. Edith got into the other.

As the cars sped through the gateway, there was a fluttering as of a bird's wings. Elizabeth, in her blue cape, ran out from the prison entrance. Edith heard her heartbroken cry as the car sped down the boulevard.

At seven o'clock, the crack of rifles sounded

on the Tir National, the Brussels firing range. And
Edith Cavell lay dead in the morning sun. On the
ground nearby, Baucq, too, lay still forever.

Of all the men and women condemned by the
Germans on those two days in October 1915, only
Edith Cavell and Philippe Baucq paid with their
lives. Although Villalobar, Whitlock, and Gibson
had been unable to save them, their efforts were not
lost. People all over the world heard of the execu-
tions. There was such a storm of protest that the
Germans spared the lives of Louise Thuliez and
others condemned to death. Edith's execution did
more to arouse people in the United States to war
than almost any one thing the Germans did.

And of all the men and women whose names the
Germans made known to the world on those two
October days, only the name of Edith Cavell is seen
or heard by people every day in different lands. In
Brussels, the nurses' training school bears her name
over its doorway: "École Edith Cavell."

In Trafalgar Square in London stands a tall statue
of Edith Cavell in her nurse's cloak. In the garden
of the Tuileries in Paris, there is a beautiful sculpture
of her. Out in western Canada, there is Mt. Cavell.
And in the Rocky Mountains of Colorado in the
United States, Cavell Glacier bears her name. Her

portrait hangs in her childhood home of Swardeston, England. And over the altar in the church is a window to her memory.

Edith herself sleeps in the quiet of Life's Green, close to the World War I memorial chapel of the great Cathedral of Norwich, in England. Her body was brought there with the return of peace. Today, visitors stop to read Edith Cavell's last words cut in stone over her grave:

> "Standing as I do, in view of God and
> Eternity, I realize that patriotism
> is not enough; I must have no hatred
> or bitterness toward anyone."

More Books from The Good and the Beautiful Library

Ladycake Farm
by Mabel Leigh Hunt

The Three Gold Doubloons
by Edith Thacher Hurd

Tiger on the Mountain
by Shirley L. Arora

Trini, The Strawberry Girl
by Johanna Spyri

goodandbeautiful.com